D1498333

The boy who walked into the castle of the Comte de Laval to take up his duties as kitchen drudge brought with him a copy of *The Practice of Surgery* and a desire to become a healer of men. That wish was to lead him far.

It was not long before young Ambroise Paré was serving as apprentice to the castle's barber-surgeon, and soon his determination helped him to reach the University in Paris. There he was trained in the time-honored surgical methods used throughout Europe early in the sixteenth century — how to treat wounds with boiling oil, for example, and the proper way to sear the stump of an amputated limb with a red-hot iron.

But when Paré finally arrived on the battlefields of France as a barber-surgeon, his intelligent curiosity and his wish to prevent human suffering prompted him to make revolutionary experiments, experiments that showed how to eliminate these cruel treatments. The methods he developed were denounced by those who insisted that the old ways were right, but their value could not be suppressed.

Paré eventually transformed the surgical practice of his time and laid the foundation for the development of modern surgery. Here is the story of his life and his daring, historic work, sketched against the background of wars and Renaissance Paris.

A Barber-Surgeon

A LIFE OF AMBROISE PARÉ,
FOUNDER OF MODERN SURGERY

Jeanne Carbonnier

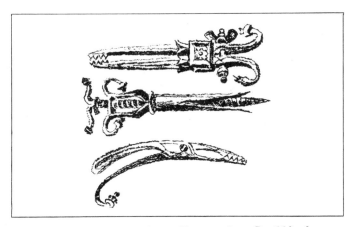

Illustrated by Joseph Cellini

PANTHEON BOOKS

© *Copyright, 1965, by Jeanne Carbonnier*

All rights reserved under International and Pan-American Copyright Conventions. Published in New York by Pantheon Books, a division of Random House, Inc., and simultaneously in Toronto, Canada, by Random House of Canada Limited. Manufactured in the United States of America.

Library of Congress catalog card number: 65-20653

To Charlotte Cassagnes
as a token of affection

CO. SCHOOLS
C651884

A Barber-Surgeon

I

The sun was setting behind the castle on the hill. The night watchman donned his plumed hat, lit his lantern, and pounding his cane on the cobblestones, began his rounds. He took a long breath and intoned, "Seven o'clock! Good people of Laval, may God guard you from evil and keep you well."

Everything was peaceful on that Saturday evening of the year 1518. The shops were closed. The town was silent except for a boy's laughter and joyful barks in the distance.

"That sounds like little Ambroise," thought the night watchman. "What's he up to now? I'll send him home with a good whack of my cane." He walked faster toward the open square near the bank of the Mayenne River. Suddenly a stick whizzed above his head, and a dog ran between his legs. He stumbled. Before he could recover his balance, a

3

sharp yelp pierced the air and the dog came back limping. The night watchman lifted his lantern. Here was Ambroise, the coffer maker's son, Ambroise of the pointed, squirrel-like face and mischievous eyes — Ambroise playing with a dog when he should be home.

Ambroise ran to the dog and kneeled. He took the injured paw in his hands, and without looking up he said, "My luck you are here. Come closer. I need your lantern to see what's wrong."

"Ambroise, time to go home."

"Oh, it's bleeding."

"Ambroise, go home."

"Lower your lantern, please. Now I can see — it's a piece of broken glass." Ambroise closed his eyes as if afraid of what he was about to do. Seizing the piece of glass, he pulled it out with one quick motion. The dog whimpered and licked his paw. The night watchman held his lantern close to Ambroise's face. The boy's usually laughing eyes were filled with tears. He patted the animal. "Poor little dog. That hurt, I know, but I had to do it."

The night watchman swung his cane above Ambroise's head: "If you don't obey me . . ." But he could not bring himself to strike a boy and his injured dog. "Go home now. Your mother expects you for *la veillée* at this hour."

La veillée. The ritual gathering of friends after the week's toil to sing and tell stories did not seem to interest Ambroise at this moment. Nor did the

4

threatening attitude of the watchman frighten him. A smile appeared on his face and his eyes twinkled. "I'm going," he said.

"I have to continue my rounds now, but I'll see you across the bridge." The night watchman took a few steps — "Seven o'clock . . ." — then suddenly turned. Ambroise, the dog in his arms, was running back toward the town.

"Eh, Ambroise, you can't fool me! Your home is not that way."

"I know, but I want to take my dog to Maître Simon's shop for some ointment."

"Take a dog to a barber-surgeon? Shame on you!"

The night watchman started after him, but his bulk and the call of duty prevented him from pursuing Ambroise far. He shrugged his shoulders: "Stubborn and kind. What can I do? I'll catch him some other time." And he went his way while Ambroise and his burden disappeared in the distance.

When he was sure he was not being followed, Ambroise stopped. He was panting. The dog was a heavy armful for an eight-year-old and the winding street climbed sharply. Ambroise squared his shoulders, took a firmer hold on the animal, and spoke softly as he went along: "I'm taking you to Maître Simon. He's the best barber-surgeon in all Laval. He'll make your paw well."

For an answer the dog licked Ambroise's face.

"Aren't you glad the moon is full so that I don't fall in a hole and you with me! Here we are." At the

5

top of the hill Ambroise had spotted the white-and-red striped pole which announced the shop of a barber-surgeon. Alas, the shop was closed and the house empty! Maître Simon and his family had gone to spend *la veillée* with some friends.

Ambroise was disappointed but not discouraged. Perhaps Maître Simon was visiting *his* house. He and Maître Paré were good friends.

Ambroise resettled his burden with a lift of his shoulders and went downhill and across the river to the nearby hamlet of Bourg-Hersent, where his father practiced the art of coffer making.

Staggering under the dog's weight, Ambroise arrived at his house. The shop was dark; the moon played on the ornate coffer over the door. On the other side of the door, the kitchen windows glowed, and through their thick greenish panes he could see the moving shadows of people inside. Then he remembered his mother's admonition: "It will be your brother Jehan's last *veillée* with us before he leaves for Brittany. Be sure to come home early. If you do, I'll let you stay up all evening." And he was late. Would he be sent to bed, he who loved to hear stories and to sing with the crowd? It was his last chance to be with big brother Jehan. Jehan, whom he admired so much and tried to imitate, who knew everything and never tired of answering his questions. Jehan, who never threw out the wounded animals he brought home. Jehan, who was everything a big brother should be, a friend. Ambroise sighed.

He set the dog down on the doorstep and looked at its paw. It was still bleeding. He kissed the animal on the nose and whispered, "Keep quiet. Don't come with me." The door was ajar. He pushed it a little further, cautiously for fear it would creak, and squeezed his small body through the narrow opening. Good. He was in and the door had not creaked. After the long walk in the dark, the lights dazzled him. He rubbed his eyes and sniffed: "Maman has got the oil lamps out tonight." He looked around. Near the high vaulted fireplace the women had gathered around his mother. As usual she kept her spinning wheel purring under the pressure of her foot. At her side, curled up on the floor, his little brother, also named Jehan, was asleep — for a five-year-old the *veillée* held no interest. Little Catherine was playing with her doll on the curbstone of the hearth. Better keep away. Maman had not seen him come in.

One danger averted, he faced another one. Papa Paré believed in a good whipping for disobedient children. Mouselike, hands in his doublet pockets, Ambroise sneaked to the other end of the room where his father, big brother Jehan, and the men were singing and drinking wine from pewter goblets. All the neighbors were there: the stonecutter, the clog maker, the miller and his brother, the printer, and Maître Simon, the barber-surgeon who loved to lead the chorus — the very man Ambroise wanted to see.

Timidly, he pulled the barber's sleeve: *"Bonsoir."*

7

"*Bonsoir,* Ambroise. Don't interrupt me."

"Maître Simon, could you give me an ointment for a cut?"

This was the sure way to attract the barber's attention. He loved his profession. "Did you cut yourself?"

"No, but my dog did. Its paw is bleeding a lot. How can I stop it?"

Even more than singing, Maître Simon liked to display his science before a crowd. He raised his goblet, took a sip, and said, "The best way to stop bleeding is to apply a cobweb to the wound. Its fine texture thickens the blood and it stops running. If the injury is deep and a vessel is cut, it has to be touched with a red-hot iron."

Ambroise shuddered: "That would hurt. I'll try the cobweb first, but I don't think I'll find one here. Maman always gets her broom when she sees a spider."

Everybody laughed and the miller slapped Maître Paré's back: "Congratulations. You have the best wife in all the region."

Taking advantage of the merry outburst, Ambroise went to the door. The dog was still there, licking its paw. It was not bleeding any more. No need of cobweb or painful hot-iron treatment. Ambroise returned to the men's circle. Brother Jehan was speaking of his trip to Brittany, where he was to learn the trade of barber-surgeon. "And be careful to keep out of the surgeon-barbers' territory or they'll get after you," said Maître Simon with a touch of bitterness. Surgeon-barber? Barber-surgeon? The two expressions puzzled Ambroise. "What is the difference?" he asked.

Jehan answered, "A barber-surgeon is first of all a barber, but he is allowed to do blood-letting and to dress wounds. That's what I'm going to be. A surgeon-barber knows how to set broken bones and can do amputations — that is, cut off a leg or an arm."

"Ah," said Ambroise, "I'd rather be a barber-surgeon like you."

"I'd rather you'd be a physician," said his father. "In fact, I'm thinking of having someone teach you to read. Then you'll be able to learn Latin, the tongue of the physicians. All that a physician has to do is prescribe and let the surgeons do the manual work."

"I'd like to be a physician, because I wouldn't have to hurt anybody," Ambroise said, and turned away. Walking over to the door, he looked outside. The dog was asleep.

No longer worried, Ambroise went to his mother. "At last," she said. "Where were you?"

Now it had come, the question he had dreaded all evening. Ambroise hated to displease his mother. She always looked so sad when she had to scold him. And he hated to tell a lie. He hesitated a moment and the right answer came to his lips: "I was with the men. I learned how you can stop bleeding from a cut and the difference between a barber-surgeon and a sur-

9

geon-barber." At peace with his conscience, he threw his arms around his mother's neck and kissed her.

Maman Paré returned the kiss. She was not convinced that her play-loving little Ambroise had been home as long as he wanted her to believe, but tonight, for Jehan's last *veillée,* she was indulgent.

Reassured, Ambroise sat down near the fire. Above the smoldering logs the copper kettle, pride of the household, shone against the darkened bricks of the hearth. The men approached the fireside. The time had come to tell stories. As usual Maître Simon took the lead: "When I was serving in the armies of our good King François, first of the name, God bless him, we met the enemy in the plains of Lombardy near Marignano. This was three years ago, and as long as I live I'll never forget what a wonderful victory it was . . ."

The warmth of the hearth, the monotonous purring of his mother's spinning wheel, made Ambroise drowsy, and Maître Simon's story held no attraction for him. He had heard it too many times. His hair fell across his forehead, he did not push it back. He closed his eyes. He began to dream he was speaking Latin, taking care of sick dogs on the battlefield, and soon everything went black. Ambroise was asleep.

2

When Ambroise reached his ninth birthday, his father made arrangements for him to begin his education. Across the river, in the town of Laval, lived a learned man who, for a few sous, accepted some pupils. Maître Paré did not mind spending the money. Coffer making was a profitable occupation and Ambroise was worth the expense. So every morning at dawn, Ambroise was sent across the bridge that spanned the Mayenne between Bourg-Hersent and Laval, and joined other boys, who were far from sharing his enthusiasm for the alphabet. In no time he was at the head of the class. Soon Maître Paré was advised that his son knew how to read and write, even how to add and subtract, and that his education was complete.

The next step, if he hoped to become a physician, was to learn Latin. This presented a problem. Latin was taught only by the men of the Catholic Church, and the Parés belonged to the new reformed religion, which contested some of the Catholic beliefs and refused to recognize the Pope's authority.

Maître Paré faced an embarrassing situation. Would a priest take a young "Huguenot," as the Protestants were called, as his pupil without trying to convert him? And what would happen if Ambroise came home a "papist" — a Catholic? A good thrashing would take care of that. But what of the teacher? In Maître Paré's mind he would deserve a good thrashing too. But that would bring reprisals. There were rumors of whole villages in arms, brother against brother, killing each other without mercy.

In Laval, the Huguenots were not looked upon with favor, but they were tolerated so long as they kept to themselves. Maître Paré, at peace with his neighbors, did not want to initiate antagonism and precipitate violence. The selection of a teacher was a delicate matter indeed.

After weighing the pros and cons, Maître Paré chose Father Dorsoy, a kind chaplain who had never expressed any contempt for the "heretics." The priest seemed happy taking care of his garden, a harmless occupation in Maître Paré's opinion. Ambroise went to live with him so as to give full time to his studies.

On the first day, teacher and pupil sat together before an open window. It was a cloudless spring day. The air was light. The apple trees were in bloom.

Swallows flew around the church steeple in wide sweeps, and pigeons cooed in the eaves of the rectory. In the distance a mule nibbled the grass.

"What a beautiful place," thought Ambroise. "I hope I can ride that mule."

Father Dorsoy was also looking at his garden. He loved it, and next to his flowers he loved his mule, Jupiter. Father Dorsoy did not have the soul of a teacher. He liked to read and meditate. Teaching Latin to a young urchin did not particularly appeal to him, but he believed it would be convenient to have someone on hand to cultivate the orchard and prune the trees.

He sighed, Ambroise yawned, the lesson began.

"In Latin, nouns and adjectives change their last syllables according to their function in the phrase. This is called declining."

It was not an inspiring start. Ambroise did not know the difference between a noun and an adjective. He yawned again, his eyes and his mind set on the mule.

Father Dorsoy continued: "The declension we'll study today is called the first. All nouns ending with *a* follow it, and the example is *rosa*, the rose."

Father Dorsoy stopped. *Rosa*, the rose, had awakened the gardener in him. His eyes sparkled as he looked at the fence where tiny red buds pointed among the foliage. "My rambler roses will be very fine this year," he thought aloud.

Ambroise nodded.

13

"Let's go on with our declensions. If I say the rose is red, I use the nominative, *rosa*. If I speak of the beauty of the rose, I say *pulchritudo rosae*. After a verb, *rosa* becomes *rosam*. *Amo rosam*, I love the rose — or plural, *amo rosas*, I love the roses." Father Dorsoy smiled angelically. "Is not Latin a beautiful language?" Suddenly his smile froze. Jupiter was walking through the garden, trailing his loose halter. "Ambroise, quick, run and tie up Jupiter! He's heading for my flowerbed."

In one jump Ambroise was out of the room.

Reassured, Father Dorsoy took up a book and proceeded to forget all about the lesson.

Ambroise had run to the mule. *"Bonjour,* Jupiter," he said. "I hope we'll be friends." He patted the animal, retied the halter, and walked back slowly, looking at the blue sky through the pink apple blossoms.

Father Dorsoy did not put his book down when Ambroise returned. Without looking up he said, "That's all for today. Learn the first declension. We'll continue tomorrow."

On the morrow Ambroise yawned over *dominus*, the lord, and then there was no lesson for the rest of the week. In the morning Jupiter needed to be taken to the meadow to exercise his legs. In the afternoon, there was digging to do in the orchard. As time went on, the intervals between lessons became longer. Soon the lessons were forgotten. Ambroise learned no Latin at all.

After two years Jehan came back from Brittany, a full-fledged barber-surgeon. It was a big day for Ambroise. His curious mind was full of questions. So was Jehan's. He talked to his brother and the truth came out. Ambroise's knowledge of Latin was nil — but on the other hand, he had become an expert gardener.

Jehan was shocked. Maman Paré cried and Maître Paré went into a rage. He accused his son of being lazy and stupid, and blamed Father Dorsoy for his lack of interest. He decided to send Ambroise to the castle up on the hill as a kitchen drudge. Nothing could make him change his mind, neither Ambroise's promise to mend his ways nor Jehan's plea for his brother's future: "Let him be a barber-surgeon like me. He always wanted to be one."

Maître Paré was adamant: "I said he would be a physician."

"Little Jehan could be a physician."

"No. Little Jehan will be a coffer maker like me. And that good-for-nothing will be a servant."

A father's will was law in his house and Ambroise had no other alternative than to obey. Brokenhearted, swallowing his tears, he left on that same day. When he arrived at the foot of the castle hill, hasty steps behind him made him stop. It was big brother Jehan. "Take this book," he said, "and God bless you." It was *The Practice of Surgery* by Jehan de Vigo.

Ambroise looked straight at his brother. His eyes

were dry now, and his face expressed determination. "Thank you, Jehan. You give me courage. Maybe I'll be a barber-surgeon some day and then I'll show Father I'm not a good-for-nothing." His fists clenched, his mouth set, he walked up to the castle of the Comte de Laval.

At first Ambroise was ordered to wash pots and pans. As he chewed a piece of saltless bread he prayed for a miracle: "Please, dear God, make me a barber-surgeon. I don't want to be a cook, not even a master cook."

His good behavior earned him a trial at the spit. He was told to turn it slowly so that the meat would roast evenly, and to baste the meat from time to time so that it would be tender. He sat down near the fire, took *The Practice of Surgery* out of his pocket, and began reading. Soon the roast was forgotten. When the master cook came to look at it, he found it burned on one side and raw on the other. This negligence brought Ambroise a sound thrashing and he was put back to washing pots, still praying for a miracle.

Two years later he was still a kitchen drudge. He had scrubbed the floor many times, he had cleaned hundreds of plates and goblets, and finally he was entrusted with the spit again. This time he did not read *The Practice of Surgery* — he knew it by heart. His willingness to help and his pleasant manners won him one day the coveted honor of carrying the silver platters to the table of his lord and master.

At once the Comtesse de Laval noticed the young servant's pointed face, alert eyes, and sad expression. "Very young, this boy," she thought. "Very capable, too. But why does he not smile?"

Meeting him in the hall later, she asked him, "How old are you?"

"Twelve, Madame la Comtesse."

"Are you pleased with your work?"

The blunt answer startled her. Ambroise said no, and added, "I don't want to be a menial. I want to be a barber-surgeon."

Surprised at his own boldness, he ran back to the kitchen before he could see the sudden interest on the Comtesse's face.

Ambroise spent an anxious day. He expected to be whipped, or even worse, to be kicked out. Then his father would be right: he was a good-for-nothing.

The following morning Maître Vialot, the master barber attached to the castle, came to see the Comte. His noble patient, like most of the great ones of those times, suffered from overindulgence in food and had to be bled regularly "to purge his body of the bad humors."

Maître Vialot came into the kitchen and asked in a bellowing voice, "Where is the boy who brought the meat to the master's table yesterday and said he wanted to be a barber?"

Everybody laughed, and more so when Ambroise came forward slowly. Maître Vialot looked at him as if trying to evaluate him and said, "Come with me."

They went through the long halls, climbed the stone stairs, and entered the Comte's chamber. Ambroise was trembling, but he had a feeling that maybe the miracle was coming.

The patient was sitting up in bed. He turned when the door opened and let out a grunt in lieu of a welcome. His big toe was swollen and red from an attack of gout.

"Maître Vialot," he said, "I need you. I saw my physician this morning and he told me I need two pints."

"Two pints of what?" wondered Ambroise. "Two pints of wine, of course. I'm going to be sent to the cellar to get them."

To his surprise Maître Vialot took a leather case from his pocket, laid it open on the table, and chose a large triangular lancet, one of several in it. Out of a bag he carried he took a pewter basin, put it under the Comte's extended arm, and said to Ambroise, "Hold the basin." Then he plunged the lancet into a vein at the fold of the elbow. Blood spurted and gradually filled the basin. When it reached the second engraved line, Maître Vialot announced, "Two pints, Monsieur le Comte," and put his thumb on the vein to stop the flow.

"Wipe the lancet and empty the basin," he said to Ambroise.

"I feel better," said the patient, between grunts which sounded as if he felt anything but better. He handed an écu to his barber. Then he became aware of the assistant: "For you, a sou."

The two bowed and left.

"Thank you, Maître," murmured Ambroise as they went downstairs.

Maître Vialot stopped and looked at Ambroise. "You did not flinch," he said. "The sight of blood does not frighten you?"

"No," said Ambroise. "I've taken care of many injured animals."

Maître Vialot laughed: "It must have toughened you." He paused as if thinking, then said, "Don't go back to the kitchen. Come with me. I'll take you as my apprentice."

The miracle had happened.

3

Loud bangs on the door woke Ambroise. He sighed, turned over, pulled his nightcap down to cover his ears, drew the thin blanket over his head, and proceeded to forget the banging. At twelve years of age it is hard to rise before dawn when it is cold. Suddenly his coverlet was snatched off and a firm hand slapped his face: "You, idler. It's market day. Clients are already coming and you are asleep."

"What a shrill voice," Ambroise thought. He rubbed his eyes and sat up on his cot. Madame Vialot was standing over him. Her cheeks were flushed, her eyes sparkling with anger. Her hair stood out stiffly in paper curlers. Her quick hand was rising again.

"Aaaah," Ambroise yawned. But he was alert enough to avoid another slap, and got up. "I'll take care of the customers," he said and grabbed his doublet. At the door, he stopped. The cold air made him shiver. He glanced back. The menacing hand was up again. He did not wait, but ran to the shop.

It was just five days since he had swapped the spit for the razor, and already Ambroise was not sure the change had been for the better. The lot of a barber's apprentice was not much different from that of a kitchen drudge. Poorly fed — Madame Vialot saw to that — poorly housed in the woodshed, he had to be ready for any task at any time. All he had been taught so far was how to trim a beard, shave a chin, and heat the curling iron to the right temperature, testing it near his cheek. Not one injury, not one fracture, not even the slightest little wound had come his way. Ambroise thought he had seen a wider variety of ailments when he took care of stray dogs and homeless cats.

He had been told not to touch any of the books in his master's shop. The thought of borrowing one at night when everybody was asleep had crossed his mind. The trouble was, the shed was dark. Candles were a luxury and not to be taken from the house. Madame Vialot took care of them, counted them, measured them, and looked at the wicks to be sure they had not been used without her permission. And the Maître kept him hopping from morning to night.

"Ambroise, put the irons on the fire and curl this wig."

"Ambroise, clean the floor. Get some logs."

"Ambroise, get my kit. I have to go and see a man who caught his foot under his plow."

That time Ambroise perked up. Surgery at last. But he was not invited to come along. At this point he began to doubt the miracle. He handed the kit to Maître Vialot and saw him take a key from his doublet. With it he opened the door to a room where no one else was admitted. Ambroise tried to follow him, but Maître Vialot closed the door quickly. Two minutes later he came out with a jar in his hand, and left.

Ambroise was on edge to find out what was in the room, but he felt the time had not come for questions. He went back to the shop to shave a three-days' growth of beard from a farmer's face.

Several weeks and many curlings later, Maître Vialot at last praised his work: "Your hand is light and quick. The customers like your touch. I think you are ready for some teaching." Maître Vialot took the key from his pocket and opened the door to the mysterious room.

Ambroise's brown eyes shone, not with pride at being praised, but with deep curiosity. The room was bare except for a pot on a small stove in the fireplace and several jars on a shelf. Ambroise looked about, his mind full of questions, but he kept mum. He knew that Maître Vialot would speak when he was ready. He put his hands behind his back and tried to read the inscriptions on the jars. They were in Latin. He could not understand a word. Shame filled him at the memory of his missed opportunity.

Maître Vialot pointed to a jar: "This is mummy powder from Egyptian mummies. It is used to clot the blood inside the body when a disease has invaded it. It stops the malady from spreading through the whole system."

Ambroise looked at the grayish powder with interest and said nothing. He had no idea what Egyptian mummies were.

Maître Vialot pointed to another jar: "My most precious possession. This is the rarest of all remedies and the most powerful of them all. It is the universal remedy for poisoning. It is the ground horn of a rare animal, the unicorn."

"What is a unicorn?"

"It is a strange beast. The ancients called it *monoceros,* one-horn. It resembles a deer and has a single horn on its nose. Very few people have seen it and it is very difficult to catch. The powder made from its horn counteracts the most powerful poison."

Ambroise lifted his hand as if he wanted to stroke the jar, but Maître Vialot stopped him: "Don't touch it. It is almost magical." Ambroise put his hands behind his back again and turned around, afraid even to look at it. Near the window the sun's rays played on a large glass jar in which some blackish worms were swimming. "Ah," he said, "leeches. I know them. They cling to your legs when you walk through a puddle and you have to pull them off or else they'll suck your blood."

23

"Right you are. We use leeches to draw blood."

"What is the difference from blood-letting with the lancet?"

"Blood-letting purges the entire body of bad humors, but when there is a congested spot which has to be rid of impurities, leeches are better. They act

on that very spot. For example, if a man has a congestion of the brain I put leeches behind his ears. It is most efficacious."

Ambroise was getting bold. His lively interest made him ask questions: "What do you cook on that stove?"

"That is my secret. I make unguents according to my own recipes. These I don't give away. A surgeon is very jealous of his formulas. Maître Simon would give his right hand to know mine and to obtain some of my priceless possessions. Now you may go."

Ambroise walked out. Something puzzled him: "If those recipes help and cure, why not give them to the other surgeons?" He could not find an answer.

Little by little he was initiated into the surgical side of his future profession. Attentive, with a gift for learning, he soon knew how to dress a wound, and how to apply a bandage to hold a fracture. His deft fingers never missed the right vein for bloodletting.

One day a man came in whose index finger had been smashed under a grindstone. For the first time Maître Vialot handed the key to Ambroise: "Take two ounces from the jar marked *Oleum sambuci* and heat it to the boiling point."

Oleum sambuci — the oil of the elder tree. Ambroise knew of its use. He did as he was told, with a growing apprehension of what he was about to see.

Pale, but with a firm grip, he held the patient's wrist while Maître Vialot cut through the flesh and removed the parts too damaged to heal. Then came the moment he had dreaded. Maître Vialot poured the hot oil on the wound. The patient gave one scream. Ambroise fell flat on the floor. It was as if his own finger had been burned. He had actually felt an excruciating pain in sympathy with the patient.

When he regained consciousness, Maître Vialot was wiping his knife and the patient was gone.

Still shaky and ashamed of his weakness, Ambroise mumbled an apology and asked, "Where is the patient?"

"He walked home. I must say, he looked better than you."

"I don't mind seeing blood, but the smell of burned flesh . . ." said Ambroise, rubbing his hand as if he wanted to deaden the pain he had felt.

"You'll have to learn to hurt in order to cure. If I had not poured boiling oil on his wound that man would have bled to death. Try to behave better next time."

Ambroise nodded silently, still rubbing his hand.

4

Three years of apprenticeship had taught Ambroise to control his sensitivity. Now he could witness suffering with apparent coldness, but his heart remained sympathetic to pain. A tense expression on his face, an occasional biting of his lips, were the only signs that betrayed his feelings. At fifteen he was already master of his emotions.

There were few surgical operations in the small city of Laval and Ambroise had never been allowed to perform any. "I've learned all I'll ever learn if I stay here," he thought, and the idea of going to Paris grew in his mind. The University of Paris, particularly its Faculty of Medicine, had great prestige and the Hôtel-Dieu, the hospital in the shadow of the cathedral of Notre-Dame, welcomed students.

He opened his heart to his younger brother, the other Jehan, who had served his apprenticeship at their father's shop, and the two decided to leave Laval. They bought a mule, and after receiving their parents' blessings, they took to the road.

Ambroise felt his responsibility keenly. Now he was the big brother and as such had to watch over little Jehan.

They took turns riding the mule. This invariably was a subject of discussion. Ambroise insisted he liked to walk. Jehan insisted he did not like to ride. This was to the advantage of the mule, and soon its disposition was completely spoiled. When one of the boys jumped on its back, it became stubborn and refused to move until the rider alighted. This slowed up their pace.

Inns were expensive and they had just a few écus. So they went from farm to farm and offered to work. It was midsummer and extra hands were needed in the fields. The two brothers had no difficulty in getting food and a place to sleep in exchange for their services.

A month later they reached Paris. It was late afternoon. The size of the city and the crowds of people milling about impressed them. It even depressed them, but neither dared to admit it. Ambroise was the first to perk up. He had no fear of the unknown when his curiosity was aroused. They both were afoot, as they had not come to an agreement as to whose turn it was to ride. Ambroise looked right and left: "Look at that bridge. Is it a bridge or is it a street? They have built houses on it. And look at this street. Coppersmiths and more coppersmiths, so many of them! Look here: only tailors in that street."

Jehan was tired. He did not answer. But Ambroise found the big city and the crowds exhilarating. He slapped the mule's neck with enthusiasm and said, "There must be plenty of work for surgeons here!" Jehan, remembering his father's shop, found his voice again and said, "And plenty of work for coffer makers too!"

The brothers settled in a small room in the Rue de la Huchette, on the left bank of the Seine River. Every morning they went out and looked for work. In the evening they related their experiences while partaking of a loaf of bread with a raw onion, their daily fare. Soon Jehan found a coffer maker who accepted his services, Ambroise was hired by a barber-surgeon, and the two brothers parted. Jehan went to live with his new master as apprentices always did, and Ambroise stayed in the Rue de la Huchette.

Ambroise felt lonesome. He liked to talk to someone about the incidents of the day and about his plans for the future, and now he was alone. The bread and onion did not taste the same.

The time had come to register for the lectures. Sure of an income, no matter how meager, he went to the Faculty of Medicine.

The clerk looked at him with disdain when he heard that the new student wanted to register for the lectures held in French. "You did say French, not

Latin?" he asked curtly. "First lecture next Monday at six in the evening."

Ambroise disregarded the scorn: he had expected it. He said with a cheerful smile. "Good. The late hour will permit me to earn my livelihood." The clerk turned up his nose and said nothing. He had little sympathy for the barber-surgeons.

Six in the evening. That meant a long day, but Ambroise was full of energy and ambition. Up before dawn, he rushed to the shop. Rebellious manes and tough beards were his lot until the master arrived, his head topped with the headdress of his rank, a black beret with white plumes. The master alone took care of sores and wounds, incised boils and did blood-letting.

"I'm doing less than I did at Laval," lamented Ambroise. "I wish I could enter the Hôtel-Dieu." But the hospital took only a limited number of students and there was no opening for the present.

Occasionally he used his knowledge of surgery when the master refused to go to a distant home. Invariably, it was to apply leeches or to dress a sore. His youth and his endurance enabled him to cope with the strenuous routine. He slept in his room in the Rue de la Huchette, but took his meals at the shop. The food was no better than at Maître Vialot's, but perhaps a little more filling than the tiny dish of beans the stingy Madame Vialot used to serve.

The afternoon was less hectic. This gave Ambroise time to read and study. Seated on the floor, he opened his books on surgery and anatomy and got lost in the old masters' writings until a rough voice called, "Cut my hair." Or it might be a lady who needed to have her hair curled for a ball. Then Ambroise closed Galen or Vigo with a sigh and took up the scissors or the curling iron.

"Not very talkative, your young assistant," was the usual comment of the clients to the master. "But he is quick and skillful." This always amused Ambroise. "If I'm quick," he thought, "it is because I want to go back to my reading. As to being skillful . . . thank you for the compliment. I wish you'd ask me to take care of a fracture, so I could really show you how skillful I am."

The first day he was to attend a lecture, he found the afternoon endless. He almost pushed the last client out, forgot to eat, and ran all the way to the Faculty.

The class held in Latin had ended and the medical students had gathered before the building. Filled with their own importance, they looked down on the incoming students, the lowly barber-surgeons, who used the lancet and the knife and spoke French only. Ambroise ignored their jibes, walked past their group quickly, and entered the amphitheater. Facing the tiers there was a chair on a platform and, at its feet, a slab with a cadaver. Next to the chair, a large book had been placed on an easel.

Ambroise sat down in the upper row. No one paid any attention to him. The students were exchanging greetings and jokes and preparing to take notes. Ambroise saw they had all brought quills, paper, and a small inkholder fastened to their belts. He alone had come empty-handed. That did not worry him. He had a good memory and promised himself to transcribe the lesson later at home.

"May I offer you one of my quills?"

Ambroise had not noticed a latecomer who had sat down near him.

"No, thank you."

"But you'll have to take notes. I have more paper than I need, and you could use my ink too."

"Very kind of you."

"My name is Théodore de Herry. I'm a stranger here."

"So am I. My name is Ambroise Paré, from Laval."

A deep voice interrupted them: "Silence." Two men dressed in black robes appeared. They hit the floor with their canes and repeated, "Silence." This announced the arrival of the professor. He made an imposing figure with his red robe and ermine collar, his head topped with a square red bonnet. Following him came the "prosector," a surgeon-barber in charge of the dissection.

The students rose and applauded. The professor acknowledged the greeting with a quick nod and sat down in the chair. The two assistants, their canes resting on their right shoulders, stood at attention on either side of him. At a sign from the professor the easel was brought near him and the lesson began:

"Gentlemen, today I'll read and comment on the third chapter of Galen's *Anatomy*."

At that very moment Ambroise was transported to a different world. It was as if curling irons and razors had never existed. His eyes fixed on the professor, he listened intently.

When the reading was finished, the prosector came forward for the practical lesson. Armed with a small hammer, a saw, and a knife, he opened the cadaver. From his elevated chair, as from a throne, the professor explained what the prosector was doing and described the organs as they were exposed to view.

At first the stench and the ghastly sight affected Ambroise. He fought down the repulsion he felt, saying to himself, "Am I to faint as I did when I first saw an operation? Pain does not concern me here. Disgust? Why should I be so sensitive, I who want to be a surgeon?" And bracing himself, he let his interest overcome his distaste.

5

Professor Jacques Dubois — the Latin-speaking students called him Maître Sylvius — arrived for his lecture in an unpleasant state of mind. To make things worse, the prosector was late. Lateness always made Maître Sylvius lose his temper. Today he was ready to rebuke not only the prosector but the students as well, especially the one who had a talent for annoying him. Always in the front row, he munched a chunk of bread during the first part of the lecture and never asked questions or took notes, which prompted Maître Sylvius to think that maybe the annoying student did not know how to read or write. His interest seemed centered on dissection alone. As soon as the prosector appeared, the deep wrinkle between his eyes grew deeper, he leaned forward so as to see better, and never moved until the end of the session.

34

"He won't amount to anything," was Maître Sylvius' judgment. "Anatomy is not all. One must know the ancients' opinions. If he does not take notes, how can he remember what I have read? Either he is stupid or he has a prodigious memory. I'm inclined to think he is stupid, a stupid peasant. That is right: he is a peasant — from Laval, I think. His ruddy complexion shows it. If I catch him with his bread today, I'll invite him to do his chewing outside."

The prosector was received with an explosion of harsh invective, and Maître Sylvius entered the amphitheater near the boiling point. He looked at the front row. The annoying student was there, but today he was not munching. Maître Sylvius felt frustrated: "I'll catch him on something else. I'll question him — we'll see." He stared at the boy and the boy's face brightened, as though he had mistaken the stern gaze for a sign of recognition. For the first time Maître Sylvius noticed his intelligent eyes and expressive features, and he had to admit to himself that the annoying student did not look so stupid after all. Nevertheless he reserved his judgment.

Contrary to his practice, he interrupted his reading several times, and each time it was to question Ambroise. His answers were more than satisfactory. They showed a knowledge of what had been explained in class and also of other authors. The annoying student was no longer annoying — he was interesting. C651884 CO. SCHOOLS

After the dissection, just before Maître Sylvius left

the chair with the prescribed ceremonial, he pointed at Ambroise and said, "Meet me in the hall."

Ambroise at once became the center of attention. The students surrounded him, asking, "What could he want? Why does he want to see you?"

Théodore de Herry seemed concerned. "Your answers were correct as far as I can tell, although I do not know some of the subjects. If you had not pleased the professor, he would have told you so in no uncertain terms. I'm sure he was satisfied."

"Thank you," said Ambroise and he hastened to the hall, more anxious than he cared to show.

Maître Sylvius' manner was quite different when he was not teaching. He greeted Ambroise cordially and asked him about his previous experience. Very much at ease, Ambroise told him of his youth, how Maître Vialot had become interested and taken him into his shop. He was not ashamed to admit that he had fainted once. He did not hide his dislike of hurting the patient even when it was necessary.

While he talked, Maître Sylvius observed the student's long and graceful fingers. "You have the hands of a surgeon," he said. "You should succeed. What is your main interest?"

"The study of the human body, of course, but there is more to that than knowing the position of the organs in a corpse. It is the way they work in the living that fascinates me."

"From your answers in the class, I have the impression you have read much. I begin to see why you never take notes. You know Galen well."

"I do, almost by heart, and Vigo also. I read Galen in translation — I know no Greek and no Latin. There is still much to learn, much more than what we find in Galen."

Maître Sylvius frowned: "Galen's knowledge is complete and definite. There is nothing else to discover. He has seen everything."

So far, Ambroise had spoken in a low tone. Now he raised his voice: "His knowledge seems complete, but definite, no. His writings open windows through which we'll find the truth."

Maître Sylvius was shocked at the boldness of the remark. "Beware of pride, young man. There is pride in your rebellion against the ancients, and pride is the first of the seven deadly sins."

"It is not pride but humility that dictates these thoughts. We don't know much and we must try to know more."

Maître Sylvius' feelings were divided between irritation and interest. The latter was the stronger. "Paré, I want to help you. We'll continue this conversation soon. I might have something to tell you."

There was a hint of encouragement in these words. Ambroise bowed and departed. To the students who were waiting outside the building he waved gaily and said, "He did not chop off my head." And, with Théodore de Herry, he walked away.

The following day was Sunday, the day of rest.

Beards and manes could grow all they wanted and women's hair could stay straight. Ambroise did not want to think of them. After going to church — for he did not want anyone to know that his sympathy went to the Huguenots — he walked to the banks of the Seine, as he often did when he was not working.

Before him the towers of Notre-Dame dominated the small houses on the island, the Ile de la Cité. Above the river rose the grim walls of the Hôtel-Dieu, their image reflected in the quiet waters. Near the portals, the scows that brought wheat and wool to the hospital were moored. Half immersed, slant slabs shone under the spring sun, worn smooth from the scrubbing and beating of the novices who washed the hospital linen. Carried on the soft breeze, the voices of the nuns singing in the chapel mingled with the clear splashing of the small waves against the slabs. Ambroise noticed that the level of the river was higher than usual. "The basement will be flooded soon," he thought. He sat down on the grass, took a book from his doublet, and began reading.

"Bonjour, Ambroise." The voice was familiar. It was that of an old boatman whose raft plied between the left bank and the island. He and Ambroise often talked to each other.

Ambroise replied, *"Bonjour,* Denis," and closed his book. "A beautiful day. What is on your mind?"

Denis squinted and looked at the water: "The Seine is high today. That means I'll make money soon."

"Fishing?"

"Yes, fishing. But not for fish. When the novices wash tomorrow at dawn, the water will be higher and the current will be swift. Their sheets will be swept away. Then I'll go fishing. I get a sou for each sheet I catch. If a nun follows her sheet, I get two sous for pulling her out of the water."

"Poor girls," said Ambroise. "I have seen them during the winter, fighting with the ice floes to do their washing. For their sake I hope none of them lose their balance, but in the interest of your purse I hope the fishing is good."

"They wash between eight and nine hundred sheets a week. If the snow melts fast upstream and if it gets windy, I'll be rich before summer."

"Coldhearted man," laughed Ambroise, slapping Denis on the shoulder. "I'll tell the Mother Superior when I get to be a student at the Hôtel-Dieu."

"Your dream," said Denis.

"My dream," repeated Ambroise, "my dream and my prayer. May it be answered."

6

Since Ambroise Paré had been singled out by Maître Sylvius the students showed him consideration. They talked to him, and tried to make him join them when they invaded the taverns after class. But Ambroise always refused. He preferred being alone, although solitude weighed on him. He missed the companionship of his brother.

He often walked home with Théodore de Herry, whose serious mind appealed to him. He and Théodore had much in common. Both were the sons of artisans. Théodore's father was a stonecutter from Blois in the Loire Valley and, like the elder Paré, had been disappointed when his son did not fulfill his expectations. Théodore had refused to continue a long line of stonecutters and had run away from home. Like Ambroise, he had to earn his livelihood, first as a servant and now as an apprentice barber-surgeon.

Drawn to each other by their similar experiences, they enjoyed talking and laughing about them, but recently Ambroise had been different. He did not speak much and when he did it was to wonder about Maître Sylvius' words: "I might have something to tell you."

"What could it mean? It sounded like a promise. Do you think he'll remember it?"

Théodore's answer was invariably encouraging: "He will. Maître Sylvius has always kept his word."

"I know, but perhaps he has forgotten his word."

"Be patient. He'll call you when he is ready to tell you that 'something' you're fretting about. It will be soon."

Soon was not enough. At each lecture Ambroise waited for at least a glance of recognition, but the Maître was as impersonal as ever. Ambroise had given up all hope when one evening, at the beginning of class, the longed-for words rang through the amphitheater: "Paré, don't leave without seeing me."

Ambroise looked at Théodore, and they both smiled broadly. Ambroise's worries disappeared instantly. In fact, it was as if they never had existed. He felt so elated that he crammed his daily chunk of bread into his pocket — he was not hungry any more. He tried to control his thoughts but could not concentrate on the lesson. In spite of his efforts his imagination carried him away. These last minutes of waiting were worse than the whole of the preceding weeks.

He left the amphitheater in a hurry and ran to the hall. A few minutes later Maître Sylvius arrived, and his words hit Ambroise almost physically: "Paré, I have arranged for you to be admitted at the Hôtel-Dieu as an apprentice barber-surgeon."

The shock was such that to the end of his life Paré could not remember what he answered. In a daze he heard Maître Sylvius say, "I went to your shop yesterday and talked to your master. He has only praise for you and is willing to release you. Go and see Mother Superior Hélène tomorrow."

This, Paré remembered clearly.

His mind afire, he ran out of the building looking for Théodore. Théodore was not alone. The whole class was waiting: "What news? What did he tell you? What happened?"

Panting under the stress, Ambroise made a wide gesture. He took a deep breath and announced, "I've been admitted to the Hôtel-Dieu as an apprentice barber-surgeon."

Cheers burst out. Théodore rushed to embrace him, and Ambroise was lifted off his feet to the shoulders of his schoolmates to be taken to the nearest tavern for a celebration.

The following day, his books wrapped up in a bag thrown over his shoulder, his working clothes rolled in a piece of blanket dangling from his wrist, Ambroise, all dressed up in his Sunday outfit, went to the cove where he knew he would find Denis and his raft. In one breath he told him of his new position and asked him to take him across. As he was fumbling in his pocket, Denis stopped him: "I take no money from a friend. May this very small gift bring you good luck. Let's go," and bending over his oar, he pulled his raft from the shore.

From afar they could see the Hôtel-Dieu port, crowded with scows and barges piled high with wheat and lumber, and they had to wait for a place at the mooring. As they were chatting idly, a boat passed them, filled with praying and chanting women. At the prow a heavily veiled girl was kneeling. Denis remarked, "A new novice. Then the side portal will be open. Let's follow them." And he manned his raft in their wake.

Denis was right: the side portal was open. On the stone stairs that led from it to the water a procession of nuns had gathered. The flickering flames of their candles lent a bright note to the dark scene. Dark was the hall behind them, dark their garb, dark the cloudy sky.

The girl kneeling at the prow got up. She kissed her companions and, alone, climbed the steps. At the top she knelt again before one of the nuns.

"Mother Superior Hélène-la-Petite," announced Denis, pointing her out to Ambroise. "She has been prioress of the Augustines for fifty years, and I am told she has the wisdom of her age and the energy of a young man."

Mother Hélène made the girl rise, gave her her own candle, and they walked under the pointed arch into the convent.

Quickly Denis pushed his raft into the place left empty by the novice boat. Not quickly enough, for the portal was already being shut. Ambroise jumped off the raft, scurried up the stairs, and arrived in time to put one of his broad shoulders in the half-closed gate. The nun who was pushing it shut, slowly because of its weight, gave one scream and let go. That was enough. Ambroise was in. He was ready to apologize, but the nun had run away. "I'd better get inside before some ferocious guardian throws me

back into the river," he thought, and kept going. Not a ferocious guardian but two nuns appeared — from nowhere, it seemed. He bowed respectfully and presented himself as the new ... he thought "novice" but got hold of his tongue in time ... the new apprentice surgeon, and asked to see the prioress.

"Sir, you should have come through the Parvis entrance. No one is allowed to come this way, only the sisters."

"Sister, I'm sorry. My boat has left. Unless I swim across I have no means of going back. That would ruin my books and my clothes."

The nuns looked at each other and smiled. The older one said, "We'll take you to the chapel. It opens on the Parvis. Nobody will know which way

you came in once you are there. As soon as the new sister is received, I'll tell our Mother you are here."

And so, through the convent, Ambroise Paré entered the Hôtel-Dieu.

The next morning, before dawn, he went to the ward assigned to him, the Salle Saint-Landry. It was a huge hall with windows opening on the Seine. Beds were lined up on each side, most of them with two patients, some with three. At the far end was an altar where Mass was said every day. The nuns were going from bed to bed and paid no attention to him. He walked about slowly and observed the patients. In one bed a man was sitting up, coughing; the other seemed to be asleep. Ambroise looked closely and called the sister in charge: "This patient has ceased to breathe."

"I know," she said, "but I can't remove him until the head physician has pronounced him dead."

"And the other?"

"We'll put him in another bed until we can change the sheets."

Ambroise walked on by. Several times he turned his head to look back: "Why should I pity him? Those who are alive and still suffering are to be pitied, not he."

Soon the chief physician made his rounds, escorted by the students. He pronounced the dead man ready for burial and prescribed, in Latin, blood-letting for all the patients. One student translated what he had said for the lowly barber-surgeons who spoke French only and were to do the bleeding. The nuns rushed to get the pewter basins and the lancets. The physicians departed. The barber-surgeons carried out the orders.

Observing, observing endlessly, Paré accumulated an enormous amount of information in his first year at the Hôtel-Dieu, but he had little opportunity to demonstrate what he was capable of until the following winter, when the surgeons were permitted to act on their own and to do whatever they thought necessary.

It was a hard winter. The Seine froze solid. The novices had to hack through the ice to find running water to do their washing. When the sheets were brought inside, they were so stiff that they could not be used until thawed out and dried in front of the few stoves that existed in the hospital.

In the wards, patients died from the cold. Those who survived suffered from frostbite. Four had frozen noses, which had become shriveled and lifeless. Paré decided to act. He boldly amputated the four noses. In the notes he kept he wrote: ". . . of those four, two lived and two died."

Spring came late. When it arrived, an epidemic of plague gripped the city. People died in the streets and cadavers lay unburied until they could be piled up in a tumbril and dumped into a common pit in the cemetery of Saint Innocent.

The stricken houses were quarantined and marked with wooden crosses. Day and night, prayers were offered in every church; processions carried relics through the streets. God's mercy was the only hope of salvation from the pestilence.

The Hôtel-Dieu could not receive all those in need of being admitted. Four and five patients had to be put in beds meant for two. As soon as one died, another took his place.

Paré worked incessantly. He incised and dressed the inflamed lymph glands — the buboes that characterized the bubonic plague. He observed the development of the disease and noted its symptoms: fever, vomiting, diarrhea, cough, expectoration, headache, delirium. Whenever he could, he dissected, searching for the secret of the pestilence. In the wards he burned incense, benzoin, and cloves to purify the air, and at night he took time from his sleep to write down his observations. By the time the scourge abated, he had gathered much valuable information and proceeded to put it in order.

He began one evening under the pallid light of an oil lamp, a luxury that had replaced the common sputtering candles. He ran through his many notes, and after sharpening a quill, he penned the title: "Rules to be followed if one wants to avoid being stricken with the plague." To give shape to his ideas he thought aloud as he wrote: "Be moderate in your eating and drinking habits. Excess breeds bad humors that invite pestilence. Do not use clothing that has been used by the diseased. Avoid wearing furs and woolen clothing; they can harbor the miasma of the plague. Do not live near cemeteries. I have seen dogs scavenging in burial grounds. Avoid fish markets, tanneries, and places where metal is melted: their fumes are dangerous. Avoid associating with those who have been in the presence of the stricken. A man, although in good health, can carry the disease in his clothing."

He had to stop. The light had become dim and the quill was scratchy. He wound up the wick, sharpened another quill, and sat still for a moment. "How can I make it clear?" he thought. "People won't understand that last statement, which is true, I know." Then an example crossed his mind. He wrote rapidly: "When one has been in a perfume shop, the odor stays around him although no perfume has been applied to his clothes. So does the plague. It clings to one who may never suffer from it."

He stopped again: "I have more to say." He went through his notes, threw away his quill, and took another one. "Do not get angry, because it makes your blood boil. Keep in a happy mood. Listen to pleasant music if possible. Read books that uplift your thoughts, preferably the Holy Scriptures. Avoid fatigue, avoid the sun when it is too hot, and most important, if you must live where someone has died of the pestilence, wash the walls and perfume the rooms."

He rested a moment. That will do for the people.

Now for those who take care of them: "Do not try to heal old sores during an epidemic. It is advisable to open new ones. Any suppurative wound helps to evacuate the poisons from the body. Do not stop a nosebleed, unless it is excessive. It will rid the body of the venom of the plague and will keep those in good health from absorbing it. Sneezing should be encouraged: it expels the miasma."

Paré stopped again and passed his hand over a freshly healed sore on his arm. He laughed silently: "This saved my life. I must give the reasons for my survival during the epidemic or I might be accused of witchcraft." The quill ran anew on the paper: "I owe my health to two self-inflicted wounds, one on the right forearm, the other on the left leg, below the knee. I always ate before visiting the sick. I washed my body daily with water in which aromatic plants had been boiled, without forgetting my nose, my mouth, and my ear canals. I always wore a small bag containing arsenic next to my heart to accustom it to the poisons, and I always kept a clove or a bit of ginger in my mouth."

A gray dawn filtered through the window. Ambroise Paré had written all night. He put his head in his hands and closed his eyes, and his lips murmured a prayer. Suddenly, as if inspired, he grabbed his quill again and in a large bold script he wrote, "The cause of the plague is the wrath of God."

7

Three years after his unconventional arrival at the convent, Paré was still at the Hôtel-Dieu. He was now sharing his room with Théodore, who had recently been admitted to the staff in the capacity of apprentice barber-surgeon.

One morning, while they were both getting ready for their early rounds, Ambroise was looking at himself in a piece of polished brass. He passed his hands over his face and exclaimed, "It is really getting to be imposing."

Théodore, who was trying to mend a torn pocket in his doublet, asked without looking up, "What is imposing?"

"My beard."

"It is time, at nineteen. Look at mine."

True enough, Théodore, although of the same age, was way ahead of Ambroise as far as whiskers were concerned. Ambroise's brown hair was thin and his chin growth far from abundant. He stroked his face again: "This is the sign that I'm ready to be a master barber-surgeon."

"With your accomplishments, that should present no difficulty," said Théodore, struggling with a thick needle and a coarse thread.

"Only one, and it is a big one. I'll have to take the examination."

Ambroise emptied his pockets and counted his sous and écus. The total did not reach half of the amount needed to register for the examination for becoming a master barber-surgeon.

"Can't do it this year," he said. "I'll have to work longer."

He knew help could not come from home. His father had died the year before and his mother a few months later. Too proud to call on his brothers and knowing that every man must face his own responsibilities, he figured that the fight was his and his only. The word "fight" suggested war. "The army," he said, "would be a quick way to make money."

Théodore grimaced. "Unless you get killed."

"But now the army is out of the question. The King has just signed another treaty with Emperor Charles of Austria."

The year 1529 was one of temporary peace after three years of fighting. François I had refused to accept the humiliating conditions of the treaty he was forced to sign at Madrid in 1525 while he was a captive of Charles V, Emperor of Austria and King of Spain. In 1526 he had attacked Charles again, for he would not abandon Burgundy, which Charles had obtained through the Treaty of Madrid. The rich province had proclaimed its loyalty to France and was ready to fight against its new master.

Europe was thrown into turmoil. Charles V besieged and sacked Rome. Suleiman the Magnificent, Sultan of Turkey, invaded Hungary and besieged Vienna. In the face of overwhelming odds, Charles capitulated in 1529, and François regained possession of Burgundy. For a while France was at peace with her ambitious neighbor and the armies were disbanded.

So, Ambroise stayed in Paris. He divided his time between the shop of a master surgeon-barber where his services were much in demand, and the Hôtel-Dieu where his advice was regarded highly.

In 1535, François began to gather troops in preparation for a renewed attack on Emperor Charles, his third war against the house of Hapsburg.

Paré heard of it and made up his mind at once. He told Théodore, "The army will give me valuable experience and I'll be paid a good salary. When I return I'll take the examination, and if I get to be a master I'll start a shop of my own." His unhappy years of apprenticeship flashed through his memory. "When I'm a master I won't starve my apprentices and I'll teach them all I've learned. Why should a surgeon keep his science a secret? The key word of our profession is 'help.' Help is a vain word if knowledge is not transmitted to others. Then the younger generation can take up where we have left off instead of having to find out everything for themselves." The idea of being a master made him smile: "I've not reached that point yet. First I must find a way to join the King's army."

He inquired, he talked to all those he knew, and after a year of investigation he was given an introduction to the Écuyer de Montéjan, a colonel in the French army. The Écuyer had recently returned to Paris from Switzerland, where he had engaged a large number of mercenaries. He saw Paré and was impressed by his experience. After a long conversation Montéjan told Paré he was pleased to hire him, and Paré was much more so to be hired. He was told to report to the army camp at Grenoble near the Savoy border. He left at once in the supply wagon of an army convoy.

The convoy headed southeast and reached Lyons in two weeks. From there they followed the Rhône River, then its tributary the Isère, to Grenoble. The whole trip took over a month.

The army was encamped in a plain surrounded by the first slopes of the Alps. It was an impressive sight — rows and rows of tents dwarfed by snowy peaks in the distance.

As soon as he arrived, Paré walked through the camp. He admired the shining armor, the plumed helmets, the awe-inspiring cannons. He could not help reflecting on the fate of those who would not come back. "Poor men. With God's aid I might save a few."

For weeks the camp did not move. Montéjan expected more units and he had to wait for favorable weather. Paré was getting impatient. This was not the adventurous life he had dreamed of.

One morning before dawn, he was awakened by the call of trumpets and the thunder of drums. It was the signal to advance. He went to the rear guard, his assigned station, and was given a horse. From the hill where he stood, he watched the preparations for the march to Piedmont through the Alps. The tents were folded and each unit took its place according to the rules of warfare. Holding his horse by the bit, he contemplated the display of the royal forces in all their glory. Suddenly a cannon roared and his horse reared. "How fortunate I was not in the saddle," he thought, trying to control the animal. "I would be in the dust already." And he compared his spirited charger with the slow-paced and sure-footed mule he had ridden with his brother from Laval to Paris. At that point he almost regretted being in the army.

He tied his horse to a tree and looked at the mighty spectacle that unfolded before his eyes. The vanguard filed past first, the pikemen and the lansquenets, those Swiss mercenaries whose fighting qualities were appreciated by friend and foe alike. They trudged heavily under the weight of their equipment: the steel helmet crowned with plumes, the thick

breastplate, and the long halberd — part spear and part battle-ax — balanced on one shoulder.

Behind them marched the arquebusiers, carrying their hand guns. Then came the light-artillery men dragging their slender cannons, the culverins. They were followed by the heavy field artillery in a cloud of dust, each piece pulled by two sturdy horses spurred on by the knotted whips of their attendants. On another hill, facing Paré, the army staff had massed. From afar all he could see were flashes of light when the bright sun struck the armor that shielded men and horses. He wished he could watch them file past, but now it was the turn of the surgeons

and their wagons. Paré leaped on his horse, still remembering his sedate mule, and was off to a new life.

This was not the only time he thought of his mule
and regretted it. Accustomed to a sedentary existence, his muscles were soft and his skin tender, a
painful combination for someone who had to ride
day after day. To make matters worse, either the
roads were rough or there was no road at all. When
heavy rain and thaw soaked the soil, his horse stumbled in the deep tracks left by the cannons. Two
thoughts kept up his courage: the help he would give
to the wounded, and the valuable experience he
would gain.

Two weeks later they reached the Savoy border, and now in higher mountains they faced new dangers. Melting snow had dislodged huge rocks, and shaken by the passage of the artillery, these crashed down either in front of them, blocking their route, or upon them, carrying men and beasts to their death.

Further up in the Pennine Alps, the trails had to be widened. Gunpowder was used to blow up overhanging crags and boulders. Lesser rocks were lifted with levers, pulled away with cords, and sent down the precipice. Slowly the army units advanced toward Pas-de-Suse, a pass between Mont Cenis and Mont Genèvre.

Paré, a child of the flat country, was awed by the eternal snows on the lofty peaks. He wished he could admire them in peace and meditate in silence upon "the marvels of God's creation." But peace and silence were not to be had. A war machine was on the march amid explosions, the crashing of splintered rocks, the rumbling of cannons, trumpet calls, the neighing of horses, the cries of men.

As they approached Pas-de-Suse, the roar of artillery fire rose from the valley below. Paré realized that a battle was raging ahead. Going further, he saw whirls of smoke lit by bursts of flame and the flash of firearms. The Austrian forces of Charles V had taken position in the village of Suse and were fighting François's advance units.

Paré's heart quickened. Here was warfare in all its

horror, killing blindly from a distance. To him, hand fighting was fair but death from the newly invented machines was unjust. Furthermore, he had read that such wounds became venomous because of the gunpowder. The words from Vigo's *Treatise on Wounds* were present in his mind: "Pour boiling oil of sambuc [elder tree] on all gunshot wounds and do the same after an amputation, after the usual cauterization with the red-hot iron." Vigo's wisdom and science were not to be doubted. Paré had a large supply of the oil and could expect more from other units.

From the pass, up above the valley, Paré saw his own regiment rush down the steep slopes to reinforce the engaged troops. Before the fury of the French, the enemy evacuated the village at the end of the day.

Followed by his supply wagon, Paré entered the smoldering ruins of what had been the peaceful village of Suse. Dead and wounded littered the streets among overturned cannons. Blackened walls were crumbling, horses were running wildly, balking at stepping on the mangled bodies. "Where can I find a shelter to do my work?" Paré thought as he walked. His attention was attracted by a farmhouse on the outskirts of the village. The walls were intact, the roof only half demolished. He entered. A surgeon from the regiment which had started the fighting was looking at three men stretched out on the ground. They were still breathing.

Paré, already moved by all he had seen, shuddered

at their appearance. Their faces had been torn away by gunfire, their clothing charred. An old soldier pointed at them. The surgeon nodded, and rapidly the soldier cut their throats. Horrified, Paré protested angrily. The soldier replied, "I pray God that someone will do the same for me if I am ever in the same condition. A fast death is better than a slow agony when there is no hope."

"No hope," thought Paré. "But why not try to help them? God's mercy is infinite."

With the other surgeon he organized a makeshift hospital and told his men to bring all the wounded, even those who showed but a spark of life. And all night, under the smoking flame of torches, he dressed wounds and amputated arms and legs, while an aide kept feeding a fire under vats of oil of sambuc. Near it, on the ground, the irons lay ready to be heated to a red glow before being applied to the bleeding vessels. The roar of the cannons had been replaced by the cries of the wounded and the screams of those submitted to the torture of the boiling oil. The air was permeated with the smell of burned flesh.

At dawn Paré discarded his blood-soaked shirt, wrapped himself in a blanket, and lay down on the ground for a respite from his gruesome labors. When he woke up, he went to examine the patients. The seared wounds were red and swollen. The men, prey to intense suffering, had been restless all night. Some were delirious, some had died.

Paré walked between the rows of wounded, a deep

furrow on his forehead. "They are worse than yesterday," he said to himself. "Is it because the oil was not hot enough, or . . ." A thought flashed through his mind: "Or is it because of the boiling oil itself?" He dismissed the idea as foolish. "I'm too soft-hearted. That *is* the treatment. Those who are more experienced than I have advocated it."

During his short rest more patients had been brought to the farmhouse. He ordered his aide to kindle the fire.

"I have only a gill of oil left — maybe a gill and a half," said the man.

"The other surgeon may have some."

"He's gone with the rear guard of the first regiment. They are pursuing the enemy toward Turin."

"Any supply wagons come yet?"

"No, sir."

The "no" was a shock to Paré. How was he going to keep the venom carried by the powder from invading the bodies of the injured? Time was pressing. More and more victims of the arquebus fire were being brought in. He stood silent for a moment, then said, "Bring me all the eggs you can find."

"Eggs?"

"Yes, eggs — and hurry."

"Queer," thought the aide, but he hurried to do as he was told.

Paré went to his supply case. "Oil of roses? Good: I have enough. Now, let's see. Turpentine? More than I'll need."

His intuition, fostered by experience, had hit upon a formula which, to his mind, could replace the
hot oil of sambuc. Something oily: the egg yolks and
the oil of roses. Something caustic: the turpentine.

When his aide returned, Paré broke the eggs, sep-
arated the yolks, and poured them into a vat with
the oil of roses and the turpentine. He blended the
mixture, and then went from one patient to the next,
applying it to the wounds.

That same evening, when he finally lay down, he
could not sleep. He tossed, he wondered, he worried:
"Was I right? There was nothing else to do. I had
enough oil of sambuc for three patients. Those will
not be poisoned. But the others?"

Anxiety, remorse for having taken such a bold step, kept him awake. He got up and listened. There was hardly any moaning and no delirious screams as the night before. "They must be dead, every one of them, from the venom in the powder. Oh, Lord, what did I do? Why did I do it? Still, if they have died, at least they had a peaceful death."

Long before sunrise, he was walking up and down between the rows of bodies on the ground, a candle in his hand. He lowered it to examine each face. The first patient was snoring peacefully. The next one was restless and agitated, his features contracted with pain. Ambroise remembered: he was one of the three lucky patients who got the remnant of the oil of sambuc. One more, then another: their faces were pink and relaxed. He continued his inspection. One was delirious: "He got the oil. Where is the third?" The third man had died. His tortured expression in death spoke of the agony he had suffered.

Gently, Paré uncovered some of the wounds. The wounds treated with the new balm showed no black scab, no inflammation at the edges, no swelling.

Paré fell on his knees. Tears flooded his eyes. "Oh, Lord, I did not kill them. I did the right thing. I did not torture them. Why use boiling oil when I can use a soothing balm?"

Following their defeat at Suse, Charles V's armies withdrew to the center of Piedmont through the plains of Lombardy, pursued by the French. There were occasional skirmishes, which meant more wounded, but there was no real battle until they reached Turin.

Happy at his discovery, Paré kept mixing egg yolks, oil of roses, and turpentine. This treatment brought profuse suppuration, which he thought good, not knowing it meant infection and that infection should not be encouraged. His idea was that suppuration drew out the bad humors from within, a concept that was not to change for several centuries.

Paré was proud of the results of his egg-yolk balm, proud of being the only one to use it. At least, he thought he was until an enemy soldier told him there was a famous surgeon in Turin who obtained miraculous cures and never used boiling oil.

"One more reason why we should take Turin," thought Paré, stroking his pointed beard as he often did when interest gripped him. "I must meet that man and find out what he uses."

His wish was granted: Turin fell to the French. Paré had no difficulty in locating the famous surgeon, but the famous surgeon did not want to disclose his secret. Paré tried everything in his power to obtain the mysterious recipe, including a gift of a jar of his own balm. It was no use. But Paré was not easily discouraged. He knew he would be in Turin for a long time and felt that the famous surgeon might relent.

In the meantime he visited the hospitals, inquired about new methods, and was kept busy with his own unit. There was always a brawl that resulted in broken bones, or a native who came to him asking for a cure for a sore or an ache. And there were his notes to keep up to date — personal reflections on what he saw and heard, and comments on his treatments. He did not neglect the famous surgeon, but visited him often, never empty-handed and always pretending he needed his advice.

Finally, after two years and many presents, the surgeon changed his mind and gave Paré his recipe, which consisted of boiling newborn dogs in oil of lilies and mixing the concoction with turpentine in which earthworms had been ground up. Paré was struck by the resemblance of this balm to his own and greatly surprised that two minds, neither one knowing what the other was doing, had hit on a similar formula: the combination of oily and caustic substances.

In the meantime the French had extended their domination over northern Italy and an armistice had been signed. Paré was about to return to Paris when the Écuyer de Montéjan, now Maréchal de Montejan, became ill and asked Paré to take care of him. Paré examined the Maréchal and concluded that his ailment did not call for surgery; a physician was needed. A famous doctor of medicine was summoned from Milan. He appeared a week later in the raiment of his rank, a red cloak and a red bonnet. He dismounted from his weary horse and entered the room where the Maréchal lay. He made the patient show his tongue, questioned him, and then pronounced one word: *"Ficatum."*

Silence greeted his diagnosis. Realizing that no one present spoke Latin, he raised his eyebrows in contempt and addressed Paré: "I repeat in common language: the liver. I prescribe blood-letting. Two pints at least. I'll be back tomorrow."

He was back on the morrow as the Maréchal breathed his last.

Paré felt genuine sorrow. He had liked the Maréchal, who had given him his first opportunity. Who would take his place? Paré did not care. His mind was made up. Whoever was to succeed Montéjan would not find him in the army. And so Paré left for Paris.

8

Back in Paris after a three-year absence, Paré went looking for Théodore. He found him working for a master barber-surgeon and still attending Maître Sylvius' lectures.

The two friends were happy to be together again. Théodore had not much to tell, but he never tired of listening to Ambroise's adventures "The war gave you experience you could not have acquired here," he said.

"That's true," Ambroise agreed, "but I have had enough of the army. Don't you think it is time I got settled? I'm nearly thirty and I would like to have a shop of my own and a family."

"Who would not?" said Théodore. "But you can't open a shop unless you are a master. Experience does not count."

"It will be hard attending classes again, but I'll do

it. You said old Maître Sylvius is still teaching?"

"He will until he dies, I suppose."

"I'm going to see him. Why don't you take the examination with me? When we both are masters we'll open a shop together."

Ambroise went to the Faculty of Medicine. Maître Sylvius was still reading from Galen's *Anatomy*. He greeted Ambroise affectionately. The story of the egg-yolk balm and that of the newborn-dog concoction fascinated him, and he advised Ambroise to publish his observations.

"I don't know Latin."

"Write in French. So much the better. All surgical books are written in Latin and few have been translated. Barbers need treatises written for them by one of themselves. And you have kept a diary. Look over your notes and get them ready for publication."

Ambroise was perplexed. His French was tainted with idiomatic expressions from his native province and his spelling was inaccurate. He needed to improve his knowledge of the language. He promised Maître Sylvius to do so, and to write up his experiments as soon as he had passed the examination.

He went back to the University. He took a first examination in 1540 and in 1541, along with Théodore, he finally became a master barber-surgeon. After the examination came the solemn oath. He swore to abide by the statutes of the guild created in 1301. As a barber-surgeon he was forbidden to trespass on the privileges of the surgeon-barbers. The barbers were under the jurisdiction of the King's first barber and were independent of the surgeons. This oath of submission had to be repeated every year on the feast day of Saint Luke, the eighteenth of October, but the barbers' patron saints were Saint Cosmus and Saint Damian, in whose church, in the Rue Saint-Denis, the barber-surgeons held the meetings of their guild. Like all the professions at that time, the barbers were organized into a corporation, or guild, independent of the University.

After Ambroise and Théodore had satisfied all requirements, a secretary penned in the University register: *A razoribus de novo examinatis, a duobus razoribus qui anno praeterito examinati fuerant, videlicet, ab Ambrosio Paré (72 sols, 6 deniers parisis) Theodorico de Herry (72 sols, 6 deniers parisis).* [Have been newly examined the two barbers who were examined last year, namely, Ambroise Paré (72 sous, 6 Parisian deniers) Theodore de Herry (72 sous, 6 Parisian deniers).]

Cicero would have relegated the secretary to the back yard. What did it matter? The two friends had reached the well-earned rank of master and their promotion was recorded in Latin as it should be, even though it was bad Latin.

Now that he possessed the precious diploma, Ambroise thought once more of getting settled in his own shop. He asked Théodore to join him in that new venture, but Théodore had other plans. He was going back to Blois, his home town, to show friends and family that he had made good outside the ancestral profession of stonecutting. And he was thinking of getting married.

This saddened Ambroise, whose dream had been to work with his old friend. He was attached to Théodore and when they parted, never to see each other again, he abandoned the idea of opening his own shop. He could afford to wait, and he was going to write — and write as he wanted. The younger generation should benefit from his experience. He would tell all he knew.

Still, he felt that his life was not complete. There were two men in him: the surgeon, passionately interested in his work, and the ordinary man who aspired to the companionship of a wife and dreamed of the laughter of children.

Ambroise was not romantic. To him marriage was but an episode in a man's life and not the end toward which everything converged. The problem was to find a girl from a respectable family.

He remembered having met the daughter of a document sealer at the Chancery, Jehanne Mazelin. She was frail, not pretty, and appeared to have a sweet disposition. He believed she would make a good wife and a good mother. Following the custom of the time, he approached her family, who agreed, and on June 10, 1541, he married Jehanne. Immediately he opened a shop near the Pont Saint-Michel on the left bank, and continued the revision of his many notes.

He had hardly had time to get established when he was sent for by the Vicomte de Rohan.

"A most important client," said Jehanne, looking at her husband with admiration. "Now all the nobles will ask you to take care of them. You'll be famous." Joyfully, she put her arms around her husband. "I'm so proud to be your wife."

Ambroise returned her kiss but said nothing. He had his own idea about the Vicomte's call, and his idea was right.

René de Rohan had been commanded by King François to equip a regiment and go south to liberate Perpignan, a city near the Mediterranean Sea at the foot of the Pyrenees. Perpignan had fallen into the hands of the Spaniards when Charles V, led by his boundless ambition, had crossed the Pyrenees in an effort to conquer Provence. From there, it would have been easy to invade Italy and free it from the French, who still occupied its northern region.

It was a crucial moment. At that time, inadequate French units had encircled Charles's army in Perpignan and were trying to prevent its escape.

Monsieur de Rohan, aware of Paré's talent, asked him to come south with his regiment. Paré did not hesitate. Between a sedentary, monotonous life in a barber shop and new adventures on the battlefield, he chose the battlefield. "War," he said, "is the school for surgery," and surgery was his life.

Jehanne cried. He had expected that. But she had to accept his decision.

71

Rohan's main units had left already, and alone, riding a horse at full speed, barely taking time to sleep and eat, Paré headed southeast to avoid the Auvergne mountains. At Lyons, excruciating pains and a kidney hemorrhage forced him to halt. His robust constitution pulled him through and after a week he was able to continue, but at a slower pace. He followed the Rhône as far as Arles, then headed westward toward Montpellier.

Provence delighted him, with its sun-drenched red-roofed white houses, its olive groves, its flowers, its hospitable peasants. He wished he could stay in that "blessed country." But duty was calling. He rode through Montpellier, regretting that he had not the time to visit its famed Faculty of Medicine, which rivaled that of Paris. After Montpellier he entered the lagoon region. He led his horse along the narrow strip of land between the Étang de Thau and the Mediterranean Sea, two intensely blue bodies of water. Perpignan was near.

When Paré reached the camp, he was acclaimed. The soldiers greeted him like a savior. His reputation for treating gunshot wounds without the atrocious boiling oil had preceded him.

Shortly after his arrival the encircled Spaniards attempted a sortie. The encounter was murderous. At the price of many dead and wounded on both sides, the Spaniards were pushed back into the city.

The surgeons were overworked, Paré more than any other. Those who had heard of him wanted to be taken to his quarters. He had operated all day and most of the night when, at dawn, an aide-de-camp rushed into the makeshift hospital. He belonged to Monsieur de Brissac, Grand Master of the Royal Artillery, who had been felled by an arquebus shot.

Paré followed the aide-de-camp to Monsieur de Brissac's tent. Four surgeons surrounded the patient. They were discoursing at length on the location of the bullet, which had entered the front part of the chest, near the right shoulder. They barely acknowledged Paré's arrival and continued their debate. Probing had failed to reveal the projectile. One said it came with such speed that it had traveled far from the point of entrance. Where? They could not agree.

One ventured: "The bullet cannot be found because it is not there."

"Where is it, then?"

"It has passed through the body because of its speed."

"Then we should be able to find the place of exit, and there is no other wound."

"Is it possible that the bullet just grazed the skin?"

"Then how do you explain the bleeding and the depth of the wound?"

These learned surgeons could not invoke Galen or Hippocrates. The ancients had never mentioned firearms.

Paré was listening respectfully — but was he listening? His eyes were fixed on the patient; his fingers that at first had stroked his beard were now immobile.

His whole attitude was one of deep concentration.

Monsieur de Brissac's voice interrupted the discussion: "Let Maître Paré examine me."

Paré seemed to wake up from a dream. "Monsieur," he said, "can you take the position you held when you were hit?"

"I'll try." Monsieur de Brissac got up, holding his right arm. "I was standing like this, facing the enemy, a spear in my right hand."

"That's enough, Monsieur. Please lie down and let me palpate the back of your shoulder." There, below the scapula, lay a small hard foreign body. "Messieurs, here is the bullet."

The surgeons, who had followed the examination with skepticism, opened their eyes wide. One of them, Maître Lavernault, surgeon to the Dauphin, the King's son, put his fingers on the area. He felt the bullet. "What a simple method and how accurate. Maître Paré, take it out."

Paré remembered he was just a barber among surgeons. "No," he said, "to you the honor of removing it." And he caressed his beard to hide a smile of satisfaction.

Monsieur de Brissac got well.

The Spaniards did not attempt another sortie. The French were getting ready for the final assault when Charles V sent more troops to free his regiment still entrenched in Perpignan. An epidemic broke out. At once Paré recognized his old enemy, bubonic plague. He tried to check the spread of the disease

with the rules he had formulated while at the Hôtel-
Dieu, but they were ineffective. Soldiers died by the
hundreds. The position of the French grew more
precarious every day, and caught between two fires,
from besiegers they became besieged. To save what
was left of his army, Monsieur de Rohan ordered
them to leave Perpignan and withdraw toward the
sea.

Dragging their war machines, hauling what they

could of their matériel, the army abandoned their wounded and the plague-stricken men, and fled through the lowlands toward the shores of the Mediterranean.

Paré had to abide by the order and, broken-hearted, he followed the army. He knew too well the fate that awaited those left behind at the hands of a cruel enemy, and to those who were escaping with him he had nothing to offer. His supplies were exhausted. All he could do was to rouse the courage of the soldiers, and although weary in soul and body, he walked with them, joked with them, always ready to assist them in the exhausting duties of a hasty retreat.

After two days of forced march, they reached the sea and camped for the night at the mouth of the Agly River. Paré retired to his tent and soon was asleep. At dawn he woke up suddenly. His tent had been torn away by a gust of wind, and his face was pelleted with sand and gravel. He got up and looked at the camp. Wreckage littered the ground, stakes had been uprooted, remnants of canvas flapped in the wind, bits of everything soared in the sky, the air was thick with dust. *"La tramontane,"* cried those who knew of that dreaded Mediterranean wind.

The sea, whipped to a mass of foaming waves, invaded the low lands. Its raging waters cut through the camp. Panic seized the men. Suffocated, blinded by the flying sand, they tried to save themselves, leaving everything behind. The horses broke their

halters and ran away, pulling carriages and war matériel to destruction. Men and beasts attempted to
swim, but were sucked under by the rushing waves.

"My only chance of salvation is to get a horse,"
thought Paré as he watched the terror-stricken men
run to their death. He looked around. Trapped near
an upset cannon and still attached to it, a horse was
fighting to get free. Paré grabbed the frightened animal and managed to subdue it. Quickly he blind-
folded it, released it from the harness, and led it to
a small hill, where he waited for the storm to abate.
When, after a few hours, the sea receded, he rode his
horse among floating corpses and bits of wreckage
and joined the remnant of what had once been a
proud and victorious army.

Crushed by the extent of the disaster, Monsieur
de Rohan gathered the survivors and disbanded
them. He announced his retirement to his castle in
Brittany, there to await orders from the King. Paré
accompanied him part of the way and then left for
Paris.

Paris . . . Jehanne . . . These two names sang in
Ambroise's heart as he rode through France. After
the dangers of the battlefield and his harrowing experience with the *tramontane,* he looked forward to
the calm of his home.

"I'm going to give all my time to writing," he
said to Jehanne, when he finally arrived there. "I
don't need to worry about opening my shop at pres-

ent. I've saved enough to be able to wait until my book is finished. All I want is one year."

The year was far from ended when Monsieur de Rohan sent for him again. This was in June 1543. The French, alarmed at the prospect of being encircled by Charles V's possessions, had invaded the province of Hainaut in Flanders. Ambroise left his notes, gathered his instruments, and bade *au revoir* to Jehanne.

When he reached the camp near Avesnes, it was on the move to another destination — Brittany. The Duc d'Étampes, governor of that western province, was asking for help. Spies had reported that the English fleet was massing for an attack on Brest. Immediately Rohan's army rushed westward, and Paré followed.

After one week of day and night riding, they arrived at Landerneau and established their quarters. A short rest, and they went on to Brest to organize the defense of the shore. Bastions were built to support heavy cannons; culverins were posted at strategic locations to forestall an invasion.

Soon the English fleet appeared. Paré was awed at the sight. "The ships were so many," he wrote in his notes, "that their masts seemed a forest marching on the sea. Then the artillery thundered. The noise was deafening, the air filled with smoke."

In the face of such a reception the English fleet sailed away without even answering the fire. A ruse? Would they return with reinforcements? Rohan and his lieutenant, the Comte de Laval, did not dare to leave. They waited at Landerneau, ready to rush to any part of the coast which might be under attack.

His stay at Landerneau was going to give Paré more work than he expected. Games and fights were organized, and there was not one day without broken arms and legs for him to set.

The English did not return, and Paré was allowed to leave. On the way back he stopped at Vitré to visit his brother, the older Jehan, whose barber-surgeon's shop was prospering.

In Paris, Jehanne had been living in constant anxiety. Some soldiers had come back already and she was still without news of her husband. She imagined him wounded, perhaps dead. Her joy was great when he arrived one night. He reassured her, explained the delay, and surprised her with the gifts bestowed on him: "A white mare from Monsieur de Rohan, a brown pony from Monsieur de Laval, and that's not all." He extended his hand. A large diamond sparkled before Jehanne's astonished eyes.

He removed the ring from his finger and slipped it on hers: "Keep it with you, always."

Tears filled her eyes. "It's my husband I want to keep with me, always."

"Don't worry. I'm through with the army. I intend to stay home from now on."

9

Maître Ambroise Paré hung the red-and-white-striped pole, sign of his trade, above his door. It did not take long for the news to travel. In no time, his shop was filled from morning to evening. He relied on his assistants and apprentices for the barber side of the trade and kept most of the surgical interventions and treatments for himself. But he did not neglect what he considered his duty — teaching.

In the evening, when everything was quiet, he went over his notes. His habits annoyed Jehanne — they interfered with her housekeeping, she said. Ambroise spread his papers on the table, on the floor, and forbade anyone to touch them.

Once he was writing, he forgot the time. Church bells pealed away the hours; he did not hear them. The tallow candle sputtered; he trimmed the wick. The quill grew dull; he sharpened another. The furrow between his eyes deepened when he was at a loss for the right word, but his French was better now. When he was satisfied, a smile lit his face. He put the quill down, stroked his beard, and read aloud the page he had just covered with his neat, bold handwriting.

From time to time he took his manuscript to Maître Sylvius. The old Maître's eyesight was failing, and Paré had to read it to him.

When in accord, Maître Sylvius nodded affirmatively, but often he cautioned the impetuous Paré against unconventional ideas. "Your book is revolutionary because it is written in French. Don't make it more so by expounding new theories."

This remark was apropos of the "corruption" of wounds by gunpowder. Paré had written: "Though this may displease the pedantic teachers of the old school, it is not true that the gangrene caused by fire-arms comes from the venom carried by the powder or the metal projectiles, and even less from the combustion caused by the entrance of the projectile into the flesh with great force. The corruption of such wounds comes from miasmas in the air which alter the humors in the blood. Then the foulness of the body makes curing difficult. We must change our ideas on the primary poisoning of arquebus shots. We must renounce the barbarous practice of cauterization with boiling oil or even red-hot-irons. This should be used only in amputations to stop the bleeding."

The wording was sharp. Sylvius urged him to modify it. Not wishing to offend his old teacher, Paré made a pretense of altering the manuscript and continued reading. After more pages, carried away by the subject, he got up and spoke his mind: "Cannons, those furious beasts! Culverins, those scorpions! Arquebuses, mines, fire-arbalests — all are inventions inspired by demons. The old war machines, arrows, battering-rams, stone-throwers, are children's toys compared to these. Is it possible that man could have devised such cruel ways of destroying his brothers?" He stopped. Beads of perspiration glistened on his forehead. His face was tense with anger.

"Why don't you write this?" Sylvius asked.

"I will, even if those who think only of glory on the battlefield condemn my book."

He sat down: "If I never refused to join the King's army it is because I could alleviate the pains of the wounded and save some of them, with God's permission."

The Method for Treating Wounds Inflicted by Firearms, dedicated to René de Rohan, was published in 1545, at a time when Ambroise and Jehanne were rejoicing at the birth of a son, François.

The same year, Charles V invaded Champagne and the English took Boulogne. Again François I had to rescue his country. Once more Paré was called to the army, and dispatched to Boulogne where the King himself was directing the combat. Paré arrived at the height of a savage encounter. Bullets whizzed through the air around him. Four soldiers fell at his feet. The wounded were already encumbering the surgeons' quarters. No time for dwelling on man's cruelty to his fellow creatures: there was work to be done.

Toward evening Paré heard that the English had been thrown back to the sea and that he could move to one of the hospitals in the town. As he was directing the removal of the injured, a man approached him: "I'm one of the King's surgeons. Monseigneur le Duc de Guise needs you. He is wounded."

"These also are wounded," said Paré. "The Duc must have his own surgeon."

"The wound is so severe and so unusual that no one has dared to touch it. Monseigneur himself has requested your advice."

An unusual wound — this excited Paré's interest. Here was something to learn, something to do perhaps, and a new experience might help him to help others. He followed the surgeon.

They entered the town, walked through rows of dismantled houses, and came to one of the forts. Near the drawbridge a crowd surrounded a man lying on the ground. It was the Duc. No one had been bold enough to carry him inside. The surgeon was right: the wound was hideous. A broken spear was embedded in the Duc's forehead. It had penetrated above the right eye and its point protruded below the ear. The features were distorted by the hemorrhage under the skin. The left eye alone seemed to belong to a human face. Around the Duc stood the surgeons and their helpers, not daring to move, so impressed were they with the extent of the injury. Silence weighed heavily on the scene, broken only by the pounding of a blacksmith's sledge near by.

François de Guise lifted his hand when he saw Ambroise, and from his parched lips came the barely audible words: "Maître Paré, I have faith in you."

"Monseigneur, pray God that he shall guide my hand."

Paré kneeled before the patient. With skill and patience he washed away the clotted rivulets of blood that had streamed from the torn flesh. He looked at the wound intently, trying to figure out the path of the spear, and finally got up. "It must be removed," he said.

The surgeons exchanged furtive glances, shaking their heads in disapproval. One whispered to Paré, "If it is pulled out, the eye will come with it."

Again Paré looked at the patient. He closed his eyes for a moment and answered, "I don't think so. We have no choice. I repeat, it must be removed." He gave orders to hold the Duc's head, took a pair of pincers, grasped the end of the spear, and pulled. It resisted. He pulled a second time. Blood spurted from around the spear; the pincers bent. Paré threw them away.

The Duc gathered his waning strength and screamed, "Kill me, in the name of the Lord!"

In the distance the blacksmith was still pounding at his forge. "Stop him," murmured the Duc. "That noise echoes in my head."

Paré hit his forehead with his hand: "Stop him and fetch me his iron pincers."

Stirred by his tone of command, an aide rushed out and returned with the blacksmith's tool.

"Monseigneur," said Paré, "allow me to put my foot on your face and I promise you I'll remove the spear with one pull."

Exhausted, expecting to die, the Duc murmured, "I'm ready."

Paré took off his boot, placed his foot on the Duc's head, grasped the end of the spear with the pincers, and gave one pull. He almost lost his balance as the spear sprang out. He kneeled and looked. The eye had not been touched. Quickly he applied a compressive dressing to stop the hemorrhage. The Duc whispered, "God bless you, Maître Paré."

The surgeons bent over and one said, "The Lord guided your hand."

The Duc hovered between life and death for a few days, then slowly he began to improve. When he recovered, a large furrow marred his face, which won him the nickname of "Le Balafré," Slashed-Face, a homage to his bravery and to the skill of a barber who dared.

10

Paré remained in the army several months after François de Guise's spectacular recovery. Then, released by Monsieur de Rohan, he returned to Paris. His reputation had preceded him. Maître Sylvius took him as his prosector, surgeons sought his advice, clients filled his shop. He had little time for himself, but he managed to revise his treatise on wounds by firearms and began to draw up plans for more writing.

He enjoyed home life after the rigor of army camps on the battlefields, and dreamed of giving his son the opportunities that had not come his way. These hopes were shattered when little François died after a short illness.

Ambroise turned his affections to his nephew Bertrand, whose father, Jehan the barber of Vitré, had died recently. But Bertrand was lazy and proved unworthy of his uncle's interest.

Jehanne's family also became a source of worry to Ambroise. Antoine Mazelin, his wife's brother, had been heavily in debt not only to the Parés but to many others. Faced with his obligations, he chose to disappear. Ambroise, feeling responsible, ordered Antoine's properties seized. He paid his debts and kept for himself a vineyard at Meudon, near Paris, and a house in the Rue de l'Hirondelle, where he moved after François's death.

The loss of his firstborn had affected him deeply. He found consolation in his work. He not only wrote, but read extensively. One day he came across a line in the Fifth Book of Galen's *Method* that arrested his attention: "If cut, blood vessels can be ligated at their roots, which means the stump on the side of the liver and the heart. This prevents the flow of blood."

Paré could not read any further. He sat motionless for a long time, gazing at the flickering flame of the candle. Before his eyes scores of wounded appeared, begging for mercy at the sight of the glowing iron approaching their torn flesh. Their cries echoed in his heart, those cries that followed him even in his sleep. "Why not try it? With a threaded needle, it should be easy to put a loop around the vessel, then make a knot as Jehanne does when she sews. If it does not succeed, I can always use the iron. If it does . . ." He did not dare to finish his phrase. It seemed so simple. A feeling of guilt invaded his mind: "If I had read this more carefully before, I might not have inflicted unnecessary torture upon scores of wounded."

The next day, he took Galen's book with him and went to see Maître Sylvius. Sylvius, like Paré, was silent for a moment. "It must have been tried since Galen and found impracticable."

"It is strange that among the many authors I have read, no one else ever mentioned this, even to condemn it. I must try it."

The two decided to ask another surgeon's opinion. They went to see Étienne La Rivière, surgeon to the King. La Rivière admitted having read all of Galen's writings without being impressed by this specific passage. In fact, he did not even remember it. Respectful of Paré's judgment, he agreed that it was worth while attempting it, "but with the iron ready, and I suggest that the three of us be present."

"It is a pact," said Sylvius. "Whoever has to do an amputation will call the others."

Soon the three were reunited as promised before the bed of one of the royal household's valets. The man, Pirou Garbier, had suffered a fracture of the right leg days before. The broken bones had lacerated the skin and infection had set in, involving the flesh and the bones. An amputation was necessary to save his life. Faithful to his promise, La Rivière, who was to operate, had called his colleagues.

Everything was ready: the knives, the saw, the

cautery. La Rivière turned to Paré: "Maître Paré, to you the honor of doing this amputation. You have rediscovered the method advised by our old master Galen: you should be the first to use it." And La Rivière showed him several threaded needles on a towel.

Paré could not answer. Deeply touched and proud to be called on to operate by such prominent surgeons, he only nodded. An aide approached with a basin and a ewer. He poured some water over Paré's fingers and handed him a towel. Paré tied an apron around his waist. Another aide took a long piece of

bandage and bound it around the upper part of the
patient's thigh. He passed a stick between the bandage and the flesh, twisted it, and held it firmly in
place. The purpose of this tourniquet was to stop the
blood from flooding the cut. Before its release the
blood vessels would be cauterized with the iron —
but on that day they were not.

The aides held the man, and Paré took a knife and
incised the skin to form a wide flap to cover the site
of the amputation. He cut the muscles; he sawed
the bone. The leg was severed.

Then, sure of himself, Paré took a small pair of

tongs and where he knew he would find the main blood vessel of the leg, he probed for it. As expected, the artery had retracted deep into the flesh. He lifted it with the tongs, held it with his left hand, and with his right hand seized one of the needles, drew it through the artery, passed the thread twice around it, and made a knot. Deftly he located the other vessels and repeated the procedure. Then he ordered the release of the tourniquet. All heads were bent over the patient, all eyes fixed on the stump. Slowly the aide removed the stick and loosened the bandage. No blood spurted. All looked at Paré. He wiped his hands on his apron and said simply, "Galen was right. It can be done and it should be done."

This innovation — or rather rediscovery, to use La Rivière's very word — raised a furor as soon as it was known, and Paré was called before the University to justify his action. The Regents, majestic in their red robes, sat in a semicircle; behind them stood the surgeon-barbers in their long black gowns. Standing also, Paré faced his accusers. He was calm, for he had faith in his method and felt no guilt at having tried it.

The Dean got up, shook out his large sleeves, cleared his throat, and announced that no interruption would be tolerated from the respondent until the charges had been laid before him. He cleared his throat again and declaimed, "Hippocrates wrote that in all wounds it is wise to encourage the flow of blood. It makes the surrounding tissues less subject to inflammation, and inflammation prevents healing;

it could even kill the patient." He sat down and pointed at one of his colleagues. The colleague got up: "If
ligated, the vessels should be allowed to bleed first.
Bleeding prevents inflammation, Hippocrates *dixit*.
I feel that the absence of cauterization and bleeding
endangered the proper healing of the stump."

Paré felt like screaming, "It healed!" but he
thought it wise to abstain.

"You were successful once," admitted a cautious
interlocutor, "but this success may never repeat itself. Suppose you had missed the vessels? Upon the
release of the tourniquet, you would have had to
control a hemorrhage, and it would have been difficult, I dare say impossible, to use the iron with blood
flooding the cut."

Paré frowned. To have doubt cast on his knowledge of anatomy hurt him — the one chosen by
Maître Sylvius to be his prosector.

One of the surgeon-barbers raised his voice: "Amputations should not be done by a barber, even in
the presence of an accredited and prominent surgeon."

The Dean interrupted him with a curt: "This will
be discussed later." He did not want to antagonize
Maître La Rivière.

The surgeon was bent on giving his opinion: "Very
well, I will confine my criticism to the technique, a
dangerous innovation. It should not be repeated. I'm
surprised there was no delayed bleeding when the
first dressing was removed."

After all had expressed their views, Paré was permitted to speak. His impatience had grown steadily and in a tense voice he said, "I'm only a barber but I've been asked by surgeons and physicians to operate on prominent people, Monsieur de Rohan and Monseigneur le Duc de Guise to name but two, and the results of my interventions speak in my behalf. Now, about your objections. They can be summarized in two. First, inflammation. There was none. Second, hemorrhage. There was none. As to missing a vessel, I know anatomy. I never do an intervention without looking at the embalmed cadaver which I have dissected and which is kept in the back room of my shop. That refreshes my memory. You can ask the patient to appear before you — he'll tell you his own story."

"Do you expect to repeat this procedure?"

"Please God that no man should ever be in need of an amputation, but should I have to do one, I intend to use my thread. No procedure should be condemned until it has been tried a number of times. Hippocrates wrote that experience is at the base of knowledge."

Paré's firm statement might have shaken the opinion of some members of the Faculty, but even these had no intention of experimenting with such a revolutionary procedure.

Embittered by the debate, Paré refused to operate any more for fear of being expelled from the Guild. In the depths of his heart he yearned for the freedom of the battlefield where he could practice his art and perfect his knowledge, but the opportunity was not to come for a while.

King François's death in 1547 did not put an end to the rivalry between the French house of Valois and the Austrian house of Hapsburg, although there was a lull in the fighting. It flared anew in 1552 when Charles V attempted the unification of all German states under him. Faced with the prospect of France encircled by enemy-controlled territories, Henri II, François's son, obtained rights from the German Protestants to occupy three Catholic cities in Lorraine: Metz, Toul, and Verdun, called the Three Bishoprics.

At once Charles V invaded France in a move to isolate these key strongholds and force them under his domination. Henri, at the head of his armies, went to the rescue of the besieged cities, and once more Paré joined Monsieur de Rohan. They were ordered to Metz.

"One of my most memorable campaigns," Paré wrote in his notes. "One day, searching the battlefield for the wounded after a hand-to-hand skirmish, I came on a group of men digging a grave. On the ground I saw a man who had received seven sword blows on his head. 'Throw him in,' said the man in charge of the diggers. I looked at the wounded man. He was still breathing. 'No,' I said. The officer recognized me: 'Maître Paré, burying him while he is still unconscious is mercy.' I could not accept such cruelty

95

and offered to take care of the man, although I had little hope for his recovery. For days I was his surgeon, his apothecary, even his cook. I dressed his wounds and God cured him. Each officer of his company gave me an écu and every soldier a half écu, so pleased they were at my treatment of their wounded companion."

Once Metz was liberated, Henri's army went to Verdun and Paré followed. At Damvillers they were blocked by Charles V. Monsieur de Rohan, short of ammunition, did not dare to attack. He ordered his regiment to camp and retired to his tent. In the middle of the night the Austrians shelled the camp and a culverin bullet pierced Rohan's tent. Rohan was not hurt, but one of his lieutenants fell to the ground, hit in the leg. Rohan summoned Paré, who grabbed his instruments and rushed to Rohan's tent. The injured officer, unconscious from the loss of blood, was still on the ground. Paré kneeled near him and cut away his boot. Through the gaping wound, blood was spurting. The two bones of his leg had been shattered and the muscles torn. Paré said but one word: "Amputation." His aide took the instruments out of the case and arranged them on a towel. He looked at the case again and made a step toward the door. Paré, who had watched him, smiled briefly and called him back.

"But, Maître . . . the cautery . . ."

"Open this small pouch and thread these needles. I don't need a cautery."

"But, Maître . . ."

"Do as you're told and apply the tourniquet. I'm ready."

The lieutenant opened his eyes: "Amputation, yes, but the burning . . ."

Paré bent over him: "Have no fear. I will not burn you." And before Rohan and a score of awed watchers, Paré ligated the vessels. Damvillers, errounously, was to go down in history as the place where Ambroise Paré ligated blood vessels for the first time.

I I

After the battle of Damvillers, Paré once more headed for Paris. He had obtained his release from the army, and in the fall of 1552 he was home again. A month after his arrival he was summoned to Saint-Denis, a village but a few miles north of Paris, by Antoine de Bourbon, Duc de Vendôme. Paré obeyed.

"A cold and dreary morning to ride," thought Paré as he dismounted before a house facing the old church where the kings of France were buried. No smile lit his face, his shoulders drooped, the wrinkle between his eyebrows was deeper than usual. His mood was in tune with the sunless sky. The honor of being sent for by the Duc de Vendôme did not impress him. His mind was centered on the news he had received two days before: Monsieur de Rohan had been killed while fighting at Nancy. This affected him profoundly, and his sorrow was increased by a sense of guilt. "Why did I ask to leave after the battle of Damvillers? I might have saved his life."

And there was Jehanne, whom he had left early in the morning, Jehanne, ill with a high fever, whom he had watched all night. But an invitation from the Duc de Vendôme was an order.

Tired and worried about Jehanne, the picture of the dying Rohan in his mind, Paré walked heavily with the archer who led him to the room where Antoine de Bourbon, Duc de Vendôme, was awaiting him.

Antoine was dining with some of his officers when the door opened. They all rose to their feet. This mark of respect surprised Paré. He stopped short and forgot what he meant to say.

"Come in, Maître Paré," said the Duc with a sweeping gesture. "These gentlemen and I are honored to greet you. Messieurs, you may retire."

"Monseigneur . . ."

"No formality. Sit down. I want you to partake of this mulled wine. It will warm you up."

Antoine was a fluent talker and gave Paré no chance to put in a word. He congratulated him on his surgical achievements, "which have reached me down south in the little kingdom of Navarre, smaller since Charles V took half of it. So, I'm in Saint-Denis to organize an army and join the fighting with my good cousin Henri de Valois."

"That's it," thought Ambroise. "He needs a surgeon." He stiffened, determined to refuse any offer, but the question was still to come. Antoine kept talking. He expressed his sorrow at the loss of Monsieur de Rohan and, without noticing the shadow of grief this remark had cast over Ambroise's face, he discoursed on the need of experienced surgeons to save lives and alleviate suffering. "Like you, Maître Paré," and he pointed at his guest. "I want you in my army."

There was a silence, the first since they had been together. Ambroise was thinking: the battlefield, lives to be saved, more surgery. And Jehanne? He could not leave her now. "My wife is sick, very sick."

"There are competent physicians in Paris."

"Yes, but —"

"I'm leaving my little son and my wife also. She comes from a family as good as yours. Maître Paré, I need you, my soldiers need you."

Antoine's last words had decided Paré: "I accept, Monseigneur. I'll go with you."

The following weeks saw Paré before Château-le-Comte in Artois, a French province near the English Channel, among those who needed him. After the capture of the town Antoine went to see "his good cousin Henri II" to announce his victory. Talkative as usual, he extolled his surgeon's skill, praised his kindness, and took out of his pocket eighteen bullets Paré had removed from wounded soldiers.

Henri listened, but did not say anything. The idea grew in his mind of attaching the skillful surgeon to his household. When Antoine left, he commanded an officer to go and inform Maître Paré that he was named "Ordinary Surgeon" to the King of France and as such was requested to come to Reims in a fortnight.

Paré reached Reims on the appointed day and went to the royal camp. From the outpost he was led to a group of cavaliers, all in full war regalia, steel armor and steel helmets, their horses' flanks encased in iron plates. One of them was ready to mount a richly caparisoned charger. As the visitor approached, he lifted the visor of his damascined helmet and Paré saw the long and pensive face of his king, made longer by a pointed beard, and his sharply chiseled nose reminiscent of that of his father, François I. In Henri's gray eyes, half hidden by drooping lids, a rapid smile twinkled as he spoke words of welcome.

Paré was certain that the honor bestowed on him meant a departure for a battlefield, and he was surprised to hear that he was commanded to go to Paris and be introduced to the Queen. He longed for a respite from the fighting, but having to travel from Artois to Reims just to be told to go to Paris was hard to accept. He mumbled a thank-you that was drowned in the rattling of the steel plates, and then stood motionless as the King and his retinue left in a cloud of dust.

His meeting with the Queen was even shorter. Catherine, the daughter of the illustrious house of Medici, followed a rigid schedule and had little time for audiences. Every morning, after hearing Mass,

she ate a rapid lunch, retired to her private chapel
for an orison, and at two o'clock, surrounded by her
ladies in waiting, she received a few privileged persons.

Paré awaited her call, and on the appointed day,
he went to the Louvre. With others he was taken to
a small room in the Queen's private apartments.
The ladies in waiting, all very young and very pretty,
sat on the floor around a raised chair from which
Queen Catherine dominated the scene. To make it
more informal, she was embroidering a church vest-
ment. At once Paré noticed her delicate hands and
her slender fingers as they played with the multi-
colored threads of silk and shining gold lace. She
barely looked at the visitors, but when Maître Paré
was announced, she dropped her needlework. Her
slightly bulging eyes fixed him for a moment, then
she greeted him — quite an honor, since he was the
only one she had deigned to address personally. That
was all. Paré was ushered out. He took with him the
memory of her piercing glance and her beautiful
hands.

Being "Ordinary Surgeon to the King of France"
encouraged Paré to think that he was to stay in Paris
for a long time. This pleased him. Now, he thought,
he could work for himself and transcribe his notes.
This illusion did not last. It was shattered by a call
from Henri, who had returned from his campaigns.

"I have thought of you, Maître Paré," said the
King, "for a perilous mission." His half-veiled eyes

made his face inscrutable, but Paré had already realized that the perilous mission meant the battlefield. "I'm ready," he said, and he looked at the King. He seemed different from the day they had met at Reims. Without the cumbersome armor Henri appeared thinner, and younger than his thirty-four years. He was dressed in brown, doublet and breeches. A white lace ruff added to the pallor of his pensive face, and on the dark velvet of his jerkin shone a heavy gold chain and a cross encrusted with diamonds. His fingers toyed with the cross as he spoke: "I have received a message from my cousin François de Guise, whom you saved from certain death. He is encircled in Metz by Charles V. He needs drugs and remedies. His soldiers are dying for want of care. I told my apothecary to give you all the supplies you may need. As soon as they are ready, you must go to Metz."

Paré bit his lips. "Easier said than done," he thought. He did not dare to voice his opinion, but the King must have guessed his fears. He stopped playing with his cross and looked straight at Paré: "When I said a perilous mission, I was aware of its dangers, but men can be bought who will facilitate your task. You will go first to Verdun with this letter for the Maréchal de Saint-André. He will organize your passage through the enemy lines."

Paré took the large, white parchment envelope, sealed with the King's own ring on a blot of wax that looked like a splash of blood, and left.

As he rode, accompanied by a packhorse loaded with supplies, Paré kept thinking of the perilous mission ahead. He was not afraid of danger, nor of death, but the idea that he might be unable to deliver the badly needed remedies obsessed him. "If I'm killed, the Lord will have mercy on my soul, but those who are alive will die because of my failure."

When he arrived at Verdun, covered with dust, his boots caked with mud, he was sure he could never reach the heart of the beleaguered city. But Saint-André's attitude gave him new hopes. His words were the same as the King's: "Men can be bought. You will get to Metz."

"Inside Metz," Paré insisted.

"Inside Metz," repeated Saint-André. "I'll have news for you in a few days."

The few days dragged into a fortnight, and Paré was losing faith and patience when finally Saint-André advised him he had been able to contact a man who said he was an Italian captain. For fifteen hundred écus, he promised to deliver Maître Paré and his drugs to the very heart of Metz.

"It is a very large sum," said Paré.

"The King's letter specified that you were to reach Metz at all costs," Saint-André replied coldly. "This is a fair price."

That same evening, when Paré met the captain, suspicion invaded his mind. "He looks more like a bandit than a captain. If he keeps his word, here is my chance to succeed. If he does not . . ." The alternative was not pleasant, but he agreed to obey his guide.

The first part of the trip was easy — they were passing through territory occupied by the French. It took them two days to reach the hills before Metz. On the second evening they arrived at the top of a small mountain. At their feet danced myriads of flames: Charles's camp. Sporadic cannon shots echoed in the silent night. Further away, a dark expanse extended along the horizon — the city of Metz.

"How are we going to cross the enemy lines?" asked Paré.

"Have faith in me," said the captain, "and do exactly as I tell you." His tone was stern, almost menacing. Paré recommended his soul to the mercy of the Lord and promised to obey.

"We'll rest here tonight," said the captain, "and tomorrow also. We'll travel at night only. Fortunately there's no moon."

They tied the horses to a tree, wrapped themselves in blankets, and lay on the ground. Soon Paré was asleep. He woke up in the middle of the night, thinking he heard footsteps. He sat up and called his companion. No answer. He extended his arm toward the place where he had seen him. The blanket was there but not the captain. Alarmed, Paré got up. He was sure he had been taken into an ambush. His first thoughts were for the cases of supplies. He went to the horses: the cases were still there. He could not go back to sleep and lay awake until a faint pink line

appeared in the east — and, from between the trees, the captain emerged.

"Where were you?" asked Paré, only partly reassured.

"I went to prepare our passage through the lines. You didn't think I was going to make you walk blindly into the jaws of the enemy?"

"Maybe he is not as bad as my first impression led me to believe," thought Ambroise. "I should not have condemned him."

"Tonight we will leave the horses at a farm below the hill. We'll empty the cases into these bags — easier to carry on our backs — and start."

As planned, they left the horses at a farm and, loaded with the precious supplies, headed straight for the camp. The ground was frozen and slippery; the weight of the bags slowed their progress. It was a moonless night and they had to avoid the bivouac fires. Often they fell into deep holes they had not seen. At one point a cannon ball hit a tree near them. "It would be ironic if we were killed by French fire," thought Ambroise as he and his companion ran to cover in a ruined house. They could not stay. Cadavers lay inside the walls, and the stench was unbearable. They went on. Further along they stumbled upon dead horses. The cold was intense; their breath froze on their beards. "We won't reach Metz tonight," said Paré. If it had been daylight, his companion would have seen the anxiety on his face.

"We'll have to stop," said the captain, "and hide all day, until sundown."

"Hide where? We are within the enemy lines."

The captain laughed silently. "I know how to make friends," he said, and walked straight toward a sentinel. They exchanged a few words, and the captain signaled Paré to approach. "We'll hide in the next village. It is deserted. My friend gave me the password. It cost me a few écus, but I have it."

"Do you speak his language?"

"Besides Italian I speak French, as you know, and also German and Spanish."

All day they hid in a roofless house in view of the walls of the city. Exhausted, Paré tried to sleep, but explosions and the fear of being discovered kept him awake. He was almost glad when darkness fell. With renewed courage, he swung the bags to his shoulders, but had to wait. The captain had disappeared again — "to prepare the way," he said when he returned. He took the other bags and again they walked. The bivouac fires were not far from each other, and the captain advised Paré that it would be safer to crawl flat on the ground. "I've no friends here," he said.

For hours they crept between smoldering fires and

soldiers heaped together on the frozen earth. At day-break they were at the open space below the ramparts of Metz. Before them a drawbridge flanked by bastions bristling with cannons blocked the entrance. Paré looked up: "They'll see us; it is almost light now."

"The drawbridge is not for us, my friend. Let's follow the walls." Hampered by their bags, they walked as fast as they could in the shadow of the ramparts. "We stop here," said the captain. Paré saw a small door, almost invisible under a heap of broken rocks. He was going to hit it with his fist when the captain held his arm. "Wait," he said, and he whis-tled three times. The door opened. "Adieu, Maître Paré, you are in Metz." The captain dropped his bags and vanished in the shadow of the thick walls while Ambroise Paré entered the besieged city, still wondering about the identity of his strange com-panion.

He was received with cheers; the Duc de Guise greeted him with open arms. The soldiers hailed his safe arrival as a token of victory, and they were not far from the truth. Charles V's armies, their ranks thinned by the intense cold and an epidemic of plague, withdrew from Metz on the day after Christ-mas, abandoning their wounded and the sick.

Paré obtained permission from the Duc to treat them as their own. "As they probably would not have done if we had fallen into their hands," he wrote in his notes.

I2

After Metz's liberation Paré returned to Paris, happy to be alive after such adventures. He reopened his shop and began revising the second edition of his *Method for Treating Wounds Inflicted by Firearms*, published in March 1552.

In the meantime war flared anew. Charles V, to avenge the near-annihilation of his Austrian army before Metz, sent some Spanish regiments through Flanders and invaded northern France. Six months after his return, in June 1553, Paré was commanded to join the Maréchal de Bouillon's units in Artois, near the English Channel, where the Maréchal and his lieutenant, Monsieur de Martigues, were fighting the Spanish army of Charles V.

The Spaniards were well organized and the Maréchal proved to be a poor strategist. After several bloody encounters the French were encircled and had to take refuge in the fortress of Hesdin between Arras and the Channel.

Hesdin was known to be impregnable, but a tight blockade did what force could not have done. After a long harassing siege the Spaniards began to storm the bulwarks. His ammunition gone, his lieutenants dead or wounded, the Maréchal, sheltered in the inner part of the castle, called for a council and asked Maître Paré, the only surgeon in the fortress, to join the debate.

Gloom was painted on every face, surrender was in every mind, but either through pride or through fear of offending the Maréchal, no one dared to speak up. The Maréchal turned to Ambroise: "Maître Paré, what is your opinion. Should we resist?"

Paré got up, and in a strong voice that rang under the high vaulted ceiling like a knell of death he said, "Surrender."

The men looked at each other. Some nodded affirmatively. Some chose not to answer. The Maréchal remained silent. Tears were rolling down his cheeks. Paré repeated, this time in a broken voice, "Surrender. Our lives must be spared for the future service of our King."

They all agreed. The white flag was raised above the tower of the fortress and the enemy entered the inner castle. The Maréchal and his staff were taken prisoner and held for ransom.

Paré had disappeared. He had gone to the bedside of Lieutenant de Martigues who, two days before, had been wounded in the chest. He felt it was his duty to stay with Martigues as long as possible. While he waited for the enemy to arrive, a thought crossed his mind. If his identity as the King's surgeon were to be discovered, he would be held for ransom, while soldiers and orderlies' were usually permitted to return to their own country. An idea came to him that almost amused him in those tense moments: "I'll disguise myself."

He exchanged his clothes for a ragged doublet and torn breeches. He dirtied his shirt with soot, he rubbed his boots with pebbles to make them appear worn out and even slashed the leather with a knife. "I looked more like a chimney sweep than a royal surgeon," he wrote in the account of his campaigns.

There was of course the danger of his disguise being uncovered, but his sense of duty spoke louder than fear and he was at Martigues's side when the Spaniards entered.

"I understand you have a nobleman here," said a man who announced he was surgeon to the Duke of Savoy, Emperor Charles's ally. "Who took care of him?"

There was no way out. Paré said, "I did."

"Who permitted you to attend him? Who are you? A servant? We'll remove him to our quarters."

The authority and the scorn shown by the surgeon annoyed Paré. He forgot caution and answered, "Monsieur de Martigues cannot be moved. He is gravely wounded."

"How do you know he is gravely wounded? Are you a surgeon? If you do know, tell me what kind of a wound?"

This was too much for Paré. He felt he should speak up for the patient's sake. "Monsieur de Martigues received an arquebus shot in the chest. I was called. Blood was pouring from his mouth, and from the wound came a whistling sound. I probed the wound —"

"You did?" interrupted the surgeon. "You had no right to do it. He'll die because of your probing and you'll be hanged."

Paré raised his hand as to impose silence and continued: "Monsieur de Martigues was already beyond assistance. The bullet had fractured the fourth and fifth ribs. The lung tissue was torn. I applied a dressing soaked in a balm so that the outside air would not chill his lungs and his heart. I put him on a diet of bread, barley water, prunes with sugar, and tisane. However, he developed a high fever and fell unconscious. Now the wound is getting larger because of the motion of the lungs. My prognosis, sir, is that Monsieur de Martigues will not be alive in forty-eight hours. Let him die in peace."

The surgeon did not answer. He was impressed with the knowledge shown by the Frenchman. He made a sign. His aides opened the dressing and he examined the wound. The Frenchman's diagnosis was right. So was his prognosis to be.

The surgeon left and reported the news to the

Duke of Savoy. The Duke flew into a violent rage. He had visions of a substantial ransom slipping out of his hands. "Get another surgeon, you ignoramus. Martigues must be kept alive."

A Spanish surgeon was called. He affirmed he could cure Monsieur de Martigues, and on his claim of having healed bigger wounds than a little chest injury, he was led to the patient's side. He asked for one of Martigues's shirts, ripped it into small pieces, and arranged them on a table in the form of a cross. He mumbled magic incantations while passing his hands over the wound and whispered into the unconscious man's ear, "Get up. Eat what you want. I'll pray for you and I will follow a special diet. In a week you'll be on your horse as if nothing had happened."

Monsieur de Martigues died the next day and the charlatan could not be found. He had chosen to disappear, foreseeing the fate that would be his for making false and rash promises.

The Duke's surgeon did not know how to perform an autopsy or embalm a body, and asked Paré if he could do it. Paré, touched by the demon of pride, could not resist the satisfaction of proving his diagnosis before his colleague. He agreed to perform the autopsy in the presence of the Duke's surgeon and his aides.

When he arrived the surgeon greeted him with a friendly "Good day, Maître Paré, surgeon to the King of France."

Paré smiled: "How did you find out who I am?"

"It was not difficult. I just inquired."

Paré nodded: "Let's proceed."

He enlarged the wound on the cadaver. "The bullet has fractured two ribs, as I already told you. We should find blood in the chest and on the diaphragm."

"Correct," said the surgeon.

"We should find small splinters from the fractured ribs in the lung. Here they are."

The evident admiration of the Duke's surgeon flattered Paré. He did not realize until too late that his pride was to bring about his downfall.

The Duke of Savoy, when informed of the identity of his prisoner, sent for him and asked him to be his own surgeon. Paré refused in no uncertain terms: "I will never serve an enemy of my King."

"Very well," said the Duke. "I'll send you to the galleys."

"I should have stuck to my idea of playing at being a chimney sweep," thought Paré as he was led to an underground prison in the fortress.

There he stayed for many days. How many? He did not have the courage to count them. Once a day a faint ray of light filtered through the barred window but soon it was dark again. His thoughts centered on Jehanne. What was to become of her? King Henri had promised that his family would never be in want, but what of her sorrow when she learned he was among criminals, pulling an oar on the Emperor's galleys? And his work? The purpose of his life was only partially attained. He could have learned more; he could have done more. He got up, his fists clenched, his mouth firmly set: "I could not serve an enemy of my King, no matter what my fate will be."

A noise outside distracted him from his thoughts. He listened: steps were approaching. These were not the dragging steps of the old man who put his daily soup through the wicket in the door. These steps were the steps of two men — two young men. "They are coming for me," he thought. "Anything but this solitary cell. Oh, for a breath of fresh air!"

The door opened with a sinister creak. Two soldiers addressed him in what he thought too friendly a tone for a man condemned to the galleys. He could not understand their language but their gestures were clear: he must follow them. That breath of fresh air he had longed for gave him courage. He looked up at the sky. How beautiful the clouds were! To his surprise, he was taken to a house. "I thought they were going to put irons on my ankles. This house does not look like a smithy." His surprise increased when he was ushered into the presence of the Duke of Savoy. With him was a man whose leg rested on a chair — an officer, as his clothes showed. The Duke spoke: "Maître Paré, I called you because Monsieur le Colonel de Vaudeuille wants you to take care of his leg."

Paré stiffened. An enemy. But his innate kindness

and interest overcame his hatred for the Emperor's men, and he approached.

"Maître Paré," said Vaudeuille, "Your reputation has traveled far. Open this dressing — I have a sore on my leg. Ever since it appeared seven years ago I have consulted physicians and surgeons, tried thousands of remedies, to no avail. What can you do for me?"

The Duke sneered: "Vaudeuille, be careful. Maître Paré will undoubtedly amputate your leg in retaliation —"

Paré did not give him time to finish. He looked at the Duke with indignation: "Monseigneur, when a patient asks me for help, it is a sacred duty. Friend or foe, he can be assured that I'll do my best."

Vaudeuille liked Paré's outburst of loyalty to his profession. "Maître Paré, let's make a bargain. If you reduce the size of this sore by half, I'll set you free and without ransom."

The bargain was tempting, but the leg looked bad. There was a large, deep ulcer near the ankle, surrounded by a web of engorged varicose veins. Its rim was hard and the flesh at the bottom looked lifeless.

For an answer, Paré asked for a piece of paper. He cut two pieces, exactly the size and shape of the ulcer, gave one to Vaudeuille, and kept the other. "If you call your surgeon, Monsieur, I will tell him what my plans are."

The surgeon was summoned. His grin showed clearly what was in his mind: neither new remedies nor old ones would cure the colonel's leg.

Paré said, "First we'll use the two universal medicines — a purgative, and blood-letting to the extent of four pints. Next, the diet: no wine, no meat, no highly seasoned food, because they heat up the blood."

Here Monsieur de Vaudeuille made a wry face. His size and ruddy cheeks showed he had a totally different idea of a proper diet.

Paré continued as if he had not noticed, addressing the surgeon directly: "This ulcer has a round shape. You know that the ancients always said that it was the most difficult type of ulcer to heal. Hence I will excise its rim and give it a triangular shape. My next step will be to apply an unguent which I'll give you and a compress soaked in an infusion of herbs diluted with vinegar. The leg should be bandaged from the foot up, and I prescribe absolute bed rest, according to Hippocrates' teachings. When the ulcer shows signs of healing, I'll cover it with a thin leaf of lead rubbed with quicksilver."

The surgeon listened in silence, watching the Duke. The Duke seemed pleased. The surgeon hastened to say that he agreed to the new treatment: "Maître Paré, you'll change the dressing yourself, of course. Do you intend to do it three or four times a day?"

Paré frowned: "Once a day. This has been emphasized by Galen in his *Treatise on the Composition of Remedies*. This information can be found in his Fourth Book."

Monsieur de Vaudeuille responded to the treatment and soon the ulcer became smaller. Encouraged and proud of the result, Paré refused his freedom before it had healed completely. Then he accepted a permit to cross the territories still in the enemy's hands and joined his King near Compiègne. Henri gave him two hundred écus and sent him back to Paris.

In his writings, Paré ended the account of this adventure on a note of relief: "I was happy to be rid of the diabolical thunder of the artillery and away from the soldiers, who too often use vile and blasphemous language."

13

Paré's situation was well established. Honored by the King, appreciated by his patients, he had everything to make him happy. But there was a constant regret in his mind, deeply rooted and seldom expressed: that of being only a barber-surgeon. Repeated humiliations, ironic criticisms by envious colleagues, made him wish he could attain the rank of surgeon-barber, but there was no hope that that day would ever come. He did not know Latin. His talent, his discoveries, could not replace this essential requisite. Still, against all odds, something short of a miracle did happen in 1554.

A royal decree was issued which outlined the new rules of the Surgeon's Guild of Saint Cosmus and Saint Damian. The surgeons were granted the privileges of teaching, conducting examinations, and dispensing diplomas, which had formerly belonged only to the Faculty of Medicine. And they were to take the name of Royal College of Surgeons.

If the members of the new College exulted, gloom reigned at the Faculty of Medicine. Attired in their red robes, shaking their heads in dismay, gesticulating wildly, they fumed and lamented their loss of prestige and also their loss of income.

Pressure must have been put on the King, for a second decree came in the wake of the first one: "It is forbidden to the executioner and the masters of the Hôtel-Dieu to deliver cadavers to any society for the purpose of studying or teaching anatomy without the written consent of the Dean of the Faculty of Medicine.

"It is forbidden to barbers and surgeons to perform any dissection or autopsy without the attendance of a Doctor of Medicine who will interpret and explain the procedure in his accustomed manner."

The College was startled. Étienne La Rivière, Extraordinary Surgeon to the King and a respected member of the new College, called a meeting of his closest friends. He admitted to having been instrumental in the publication of the first decree but was at a loss to explain the sudden reversal of the King's decision. He advocated rebellion. His words were acclaimed but he added, "Not an open rebellion which might antagonize the King and his advisors on this matter and bring a total annulment of the new privileges. I have a plan. Gentlemen, we must admit Ambroise Paré to the College."

"A barber," said one, as if the proposition was a personal insult.

"He does not know Latin," sneered another.

La Rivière imposed silence: "Let me speak. Paré has done more for the development of our art than any other surgeon, and I mean surgeon, not barber-surgeon. The King appreciates and admires him."

"He can't become a member unless he passes the examination. Thank the Lord, that privilege has not been taken from us. But how can he? The examination must be in Latin."

"It will be," answered La Rivière and he left in a hurry.

A short time later he entered Maître Paré's shop. Paré was reading upstairs. The apprentices and the aides were busy with the clients. La Rivière answered their respectful greetings and climbed the stairs rapidly. "Ambroise," he said, forgetting his usual *"bonjour,"* "you are going to be a member of our new College."

Paré closed his book and answered, "I was reading an interesting chapter in Galen's —"

"Did you hear me? You are going to be a member of our College."

"That's a good joke," laughed Paré. "How can I be admitted? I'm only a barber."

"We'll admit you because you'll pass the examination."

"In Latin?"

"In Latin."

Paré reopened his book: "As I was telling you, this interesting chapter —"

"Ambroise, listen to me. You must pass the examination to give prestige to our College, which is threatened with extinction. It will be easy. In a few weeks you can master enough Latin to be able to answer a few chosen questions. I'll pick the panel of examiners myself and will conduct the whole procedure."

Paré laughed: "It's a long time since Father Dorsoy tried to teach me *rosa,* the rose. In fact he never tried very hard, and I did not co-operate, either. And don't forget, I'm over forty and my memory is not what it used to be."

"Nonsense. It is a matter of life and death for our College, and think what it will mean to you to be an accredited surgeon."

Paré waited a moment before answering: "It would mean much. My life would be changed."

La Rivière's arguments finally convinced Paré that he ought to take the examination, and they both went to buy the necessary books, a Latin grammar and a dictionary. The following weeks saw Paré studying day and night. He fought a losing battle with the intricate syntax, the difficult verbs, and the complicated declensions. He wrote and memorized a few phrases that might come in handy, and tried to repress the discouragement that seized him at times.

On August 18, 1554, he submitted his request for admission to the examination. It was written in faultless Latin: La Rivière had seen to that. He was accepted at once. Four days later, at the house of one of the College fellows, Paré presented himself before a panel of examiners. This meeting had been kept secret to prevent any concerted opposition. He was advised that the usual fee had been waived and that he would be examined at the Hôtel-Dieu on August 27 for the title of Bachelor in Surgery.

On that day, the doors of the hospital were closed to the public. No one was admitted but the candidate, the jury, a few privileged noblemen, and two bishops.

Paré, annoyed at the entire proceeding, tired from his long hours of study, conscious of his inadequacy in Latin but sure of his knowledge of his profession, wondered if the whole thing was honest and worth the risk. In a state of rebellion he faced his examiners. The questions were simply worded. He understood them, but his mind worked quicker than his memory of the rapidly learned Latin. He mumbled, he fumbled, he latinized French words and got lost in the maze of verb tenses and noun declensions. La Rivière prompted him, as did some of the other examiners, but deaf to their cues, Paré stumbled on, carried away by his knowledge of the subject and lacking the means to express it. Among the auditors the two bishops were conspicuous for their hardly concealed bursts of laughter at the Latin of the candidate.

When the ordeal was over, Paré wiped his brow

and waited for the verdict with doubt in his mind, in spite of the encouraging smiles of the members of the panel.

After a short deliberation, La Rivière got up and announced that Ambroise Paré was admitted to the College by two-thirds of the vote, under the condition that he would learn Latin and surgery.

The new Bachelor of Surgery then submitted a request for the license examination, for which he wrote a thesis. He passed successfully and was received *in favor Regis* — by royal favor.

The tests were finished. Maître Paré could don the long black robe of the surgeons, he who so far had worn only the short robe of the barbers. All he needed now was the square bonnet to complete his official outfit.

The ceremony took place on December 3. Paré was an accredited member of the College. He was happy and so was La Rivière, whose plan had finally brought the desired result. The second decree was revoked and from that time on, the Royal College of Surgeons could obtain all the cadavers they needed.

14

"A beautiful day," thought Ambroise Paré as he rode his white mare through the streets of Paris, "and a glad day also." He had left his beloved books with a feeling of guilt but could not help sharing the general happiness which made this bright June day even brighter.

He felt that the present year, 1559, would bring lasting peace to the Kingdom of France. The treaty of Cateau-Cambrésis had put an end to the hostilities between the Austrian house of Hapsburg and the French house of Valois. France kept the Three Bishoprics — Metz, Toul, and Verdun. Northern Italy was returned to Spain, and Calais, the last English stronghold on the continent since the end of the Hundred Years' War, became French at last.

As was customary, dynastic unions sealed the new friendship. A French princess, Henri II's daughter

Isabelle, was marrying Philip II, King of Spain since the death of his father, Charles V. And Henri's sister was to become the bride of the Duke of Savoy.

Festivities greeted the peace. The people danced in the streets, wine flowed in the public fountains, prayers of thanks were offered throughout the kingdom, the imposing Te Deum was sung in the churches.

Paré had always shunned popular and religious celebrations, but today was an exception. He had been commanded, because of his position as surgeon to the King, to attend a tournament held before the Château des Tournelles, and an extraordinary tournament it would be. Henri had announced he was to display his skill with the lance in single combat against the knights of his army.

So, arrayed in garnet satin and black velvet, a white ruff around his neck, Paré was heading for Les Tournelles in the midst of the multitude gathered near the castle grounds. The enthusiasm of the Parisians amused him. He laughed at their exclamations when he insisted on pushing his mare through the crowds; he exchanged compliments with bright-eyed maidens, accepted a goblet of wine as he rode by a fountain, and decorated his saddle with flowers tossed at him by a child.

He arrived late at the gates, dismounted with agility, and looked at the magnificent spectacle as he walked toward the royal box. An immense area had been fenced off before the castle. At one end, prancing horses and richly armored knights with their squires were waiting for their turn at combat. At the other end, under a canopy decorated with hanging tapestries and gold draperies, Queen Catherine sat, surrounded by her usual retinue of young maidens. The colorful dresses, the resplendent jewelry, blazed under the bright sun, in contrast with the somber attire of the Court astrologer at the Queen's feet.

Paré was aware that Catherine, who consulted the stars daily, had been warned they were not favorable to the King on that very day. He looked for the heir to the throne to reassure himself of the continuity of the lineage. There he was — François, pale, sickly looking, with his consort, Mary of the Stuart clan, who claimed the crown of Scotland as her own. At the railing, Henri's younger sons, Charles and Henri, applauded the skill of the contenders with cries and waving of hands. The baby, Hercule-François, was there also, in the arms of his nurse.

Their lances pointed toward the sky, their shields protecting their chests, two knights were galloping head on toward each other from the ends of the arena. The white plumes on one helmet identified the King. As they came near, they lowered their lances, each pointing at the other. The King's adversary, struck by the royal lance, lost his balance and rolled to the ground, and the spectators shouted their approval.

"It must be the last joust," thought Paré as he saw the Queen waving her lace handkerchief, but the

King had already turned around and was pointing to another knight. Paré saw the Queen sink back on her throne, hiding her face in her hands.

The new contender, in dark armor, mounted on a black charger, had accepted the challenge. He rode to the other extremity of the arena and waited for the signal. When it came, the two horses rushed toward the center of the field. As their paths met, the lances crossed and broke under the impact. When his charger carried him past the point of encounter, the King threw away his lance, took another from his squire without dismounting, and turned around. Against the established rules, the dark knight kept the stump of his lance in his hands. Borne by his galloping horse, he came face to face with the King. There was a metallic rattle. The broken lance lifted the helmet visor and penetrated the King's eye. In a clatter of steel Henri fell, mortally wounded by his opponent, Gabriel Montgomery of the Scots Guards.

The tumult as the crowd rushed into the arena prevented Paré from reaching the King. He waited awhile and then went to the castle where Henri had been carried. To his surprise, a guard denied him access. He insisted: "I am Maître Paré, surgeon to His Majesty."

"I know," was the answer. "I have orders to prevent your admittance to the castle."

Hurt by this open demonstration of the other surgeon's jealousy, Paré sat next to the guard, waiting for the call. It never came. He went home, still hoping, but he was ignored. The renowned anatomist Vesalius was summoned from afar. Physicians and surgeons advocated remedies and operations. If they thought of Maître Paré, it was to make sure he would not be consulted.

Henri died ten days later, after pleading that Montgomery should not be indicted for this unavoidable act of God. Only then was Paré called to the Louvre, to perform the autopsy and to embalm the King's body.

Sixteen years old and King of France, Henri's older son succeeded his father under the name of François II, and one of his first acts was to ratify Paré's position as his personal surgeon.

Interested in medicine, perhaps because of his poor health, the young monarch enjoyed Paré's company. He often asked him to come to the Louvre to read parts of his new book, *Universal Anatomy*. But François never saw its publication. Less than five months after his father's tragic death, he was seized with violent headaches accompanied by "an unexplainable fever and some mysterious nervous troubles." He called for Paré, rejecting other physicians and surgeons. Paré put all his science and devotion to the service of his King, but to no avail. François died in December 1560, and ten-year-old Charles ascended the throne under the regency of Queen Catherine.

Soon, rumors began to circulate that the King had been poisoned. And who could have poisoned him?

His surgeon, of course. Some affirmed that the King had been given an elixir containing a venomous substance. Others, that a subtle poison had been instilled in his ear — his headaches were proof of it.

These stories reached the royal circle. A courtier had the effrontery, one day, to tell the Queen that Maître Paré had killed her son. Catherine rebuked him with indignation: "Maître Paré is an upright man. The idea of murdering his King would be as foreign to him as it would be to me. I value his services and his honesty, and you can tell those who spread calumny that I, the Queen Regent, have named Maître Paré surgeon to our new King, Charles the Ninth."

Jealousy did not cease, but gossip went underground and Paré's enemies waited for another opportunity to malign his character.

15

At first Charles was not in need of his surgeon's assistance. He was in good health. (If he had not been, Catherine would first have consulted her astrologer.) This gave Paré time to finish his *Universal Anatomy* and to attend to his ever-growing clientele.

One day he was called in consultation to the village of Chaillot, at the request of three of his colleagues. Chaillot was on the right bank of the Seine, a good distance from the Rue de l'Hirondelle where Paré lived. The bridges were few and far apart, and it was quicker to take the ferry across.

It was a pleasant May morning and Paré looked forward to an enjoyable trip. He took his kit, mounted his white mare, and in the company of Dr. Nestor, Regent at the Faculty of Medicine, and two surgeons, Maître Hubert and Maître Portail, he rode to the Seine embankment. The ferry was waiting. The four dismounted. Dr. Nestor pulled his horse onto the flat boat. Paré followed, but as soon as his mare put a leg on the swaying raft, it reared and drew back. Paré encouraged it with kind words and pats on the nose. The mare retreated further. "You are as stubborn as the mule I rode in Laval," Ambroise said impatiently, and he gave it a crack with his whip. The mare kicked with its hind legs and its hoof hit Ambroise's shin. He staggered but kept his balance. Fearful of another kick and racked by intense pain, he stepped back and fell. The bones of his leg had been fractured, and under the shock of the fall they ripped his flesh, even the leather of his boots. He felt a pain such as he did not think it was possible to endure. Thoughts flashed through his mind when he realized the extent of his injury: *compound fracture ... gangrene ... amputation.*

His friends carried him to the nearest house, a thatch-covered hut occupied by an elderly peasant couple, and Paré was laid down on their straw mattress. His companions opened their kits and asked for ingredients to make a soothing balm: wheat flour, eggs, and butter. While the wife kindled the fire, the man hastened to get what they wanted.

On hearing of the accident, a crowd had gathered at the door. One by one they worked their way in and watched Maître Portail prepare the balm. He melted the butter and blended it with the flour and the whites of the eggs. He scraped some soot from the fireplace and added it to the mixture.

During that time Paré's boot and breeches had been cut and the overlapping edges of the broken bones could be seen in the torn flesh. Gently Portail covered the wound with the balm — Paré did not move. When this was done, Paré addressed Maître Hubert: "Now you have to put the bones in good position." Hubert did not answer. Paré continued: "I know what you are thinking — amputation. I won't submit to it."

"Don't you remember, Ambroise, that the ancients say that if the marrow of a bone has been injured, there is no hope of saving the limb?"

"I know, and I take the responsibility for my treatment. You must bring the bones together. First feel with your fingers and remove any loose splinters. If you can't, enlarge the wound with a razor. This is most important to promote healing. Then pull on the foot until the bones are straight and well put together. Don't try to save me pain — forget I am your friend. When this is done, immobilize my leg as you would for an ordinary fracture. I'm ready."

Hubert did as told. He explored the wound, then Nestor and Portail held Paré while Hubert pulled on the foot with all his might. Slowly the bones sank in the flesh and their ends met. More balm was smeared on the wound and the leg was bandaged from the heel to the knee. Two splints were applied on each side and fastened in place with more bandage. Ambroise was pale, but not once did he let a cry escape his parched lips. He accepted a glass of wine and propped himself on his elbows. "Good work," he said. "Now you have to relieve the pressure on my heel. If the weight of my leg rests on it, it will be most painful. Make two cushions out of straw, one for the heel, the other to be put under my knee to flex it slightly. This position will facilitate the circulation of the humors."

In the evening he was taken home on a stretcher and Hubert bled him to the extent of three pints. He refused the food Jehanne had prepared and told her that for the next fortnight he would eat each day twelve prunes and six slices of bread and nothing else. To quench his thirst, she was to give him some wine mixed with sugar and cinnamon.

The next day Jehanne sent for La Rivière. He agreed with the treatment and took care of Ambroise for the three months he was bedridden.

For a man as active as Paré a prolonged rest was a severe trial, and as he lay idle, his thoughts were far from gay. Less than one year earlier he had buried his second son, Isaac, before the boy had reached his first birthday. His third and only living child, Catherine, was a puny girl with hardly strength enough to breathe. Who would carry on his name and be heir to his knowledge?

After three months of complete immobility he began walking with the help of crutches. His will to get well made him discard them in another four weeks, and to everybody's surprise, the slight limp he had shown at first disappeared entirely.

His friends rejoiced, but his enemies did not. Their jealousy increased tenfold when he was named First Surgeon to King Charles IX in place of the deceased Maître Lavernault. Something must be done to stop this Huguenot barber, they thought. Still, they did not dare attack him openly.

The first year of Charles IX's reign under Catherine's regency was relatively peaceful. There were sporadic fights between Catholics and Protestants, but the latter, a minority scattered throughout France, were not organized. However, as hatred on both sides fostered increasing violence, the Protestants began to feel the need of an army. With financial help from England they equipped several regiments, and in March 1562 they engaged the Catholics in open warfare. Taken by surprise, Poitiers, Blois, Tours, Bourges in the center of France, and Rouen in Normandy fell to the Protestants.

The royal army, and Paré with it, endeavored to take back those cities. Success crowned their campaign, and from the center of France they went to Normandy. Rouen surrendered after a long siege and at the price of many casualties in both camps.

Antoine de Bourbon, King of Navarre, now fighting with his cousin Charles IX, was severely wounded in one of the assaults. He had received an arquebus shot in his left shoulder. Maître Paré was called after the surgeons had tried in vain to locate the bullet. Paré used his old method of placing the patient in the position he had held when stricken, and announced it was impossible to extract the projectile. It was in the medulla of the bone, and gangrene would follow whether it was removed or not. No one agreed with him, but unfortunately for Antoine de Bourbon, Paré's prognosis was right. Antoine died a few days later. While embalming the body, Paré found the bullet where he said he would, and when back in Paris, he presented it to Charles IX.

While staying in Rouen, Paré became acquainted with a group of noblemen who expressed great interest in his work. Paré, always happy to explain his discoveries, responded to their proffered friendship with a touch of pride. From medicine the conversation often shifted to philosophy, even to religion. Although careful not to display his ties to the Huguenots, Paré let his new friends know he favored a reformation. These gentlemen, though all Catholic, were so understanding and so broad-minded that he felt no need to hide his thoughts, and when invited to a banquet given in his honor by these trusted companions, he accepted.

At the appointed time he went to the home of one of the noblemen. The guests were few and chosen from among those who had agreed with Paré and favored a reformation. The atmosphere was one of festive gaiety. Candles cast a soft glow on the silver platters and the pewter goblets on the table. Wine poured freely, the dishes were many and well seasoned. Paré congratulated his host: "A master cook!"

"Wait until you have tasted something which I ordered specially for you," and a dish was put before Paré. He sniffed with delight: "Ah, cabbages!" and plunged his fingers into the plate. He smacked his lips: "An unusual savor . . . delectable," he exclaimed and took another mouthful. As he swallowed, he felt an intense burning in his throat. "Arsenic or a corrosive sublimate," he thought, and quickly reached for his goblet and gulped some wine. Then he got up, his eyes sparkling with indignation, and pointed at his host: "Murderer, cowardly murderer who prefers a crime to a fight in the open and who poisons me under the cover of friendship." He pushed away his chair. It fell over with a loud bang. He ran out. No one followed him.

Covered in cold sweat, burning with intense thirst, he rushed to the nearest apothecary and asked for an emetic. Then he swallowed large quantities of olive oil, followed by milk to which he added butter and the yolks of two eggs. This prompt and rational treatment saved his life. He swore never again to eat cabbages or anything else in the company of new friends, and to keep his religious beliefs to himself.

A stay of one year in Paris allowed Paré to finish his manuscript on *Wounds and Fractures of the Human Head, Their Treatment and the Drawing of Instruments Needed for It.* It was published in February 1561.

The next month he went to Fontainebleau, summoned by Queen Catherine. As soon as he arrived at the palace he was taken to her apartments. She was not Regent any more, since, a few months earlier, Charles had reached his thirteenth birthday, the majority for a king. But she was still very much the Queen.

Paré found her as of old among her retinue of brightly dressed young maidens, whose appearance made a striking contrast to hers. Clad in black with a long veil hanging from a cap dipping to a point on her forehead — the garb of a widow — she was embroidering church vestments as on the first day he had seen her. Her face showed signs of her age, but her hands had remained young and beautiful, those white delicate hands that he always remembered. She did not occupy the raised chair since the King was present — he did. Catherine had a sense of hierarchy. But she still dominated the scene.

Both mother and son greeted Paré cordially. It was Catherine who outlined their plan. They had in mind a long trip through the kingdom, with the entire Court and Maître Paré accompanying them. "It might be a victory," she said, "to take towns by force, but a king must know his people and the people must know their king."

"She is wise," thought Paré, "wise and shrewd." He looked at Charles, whose placid features showed no interest in his mother's plan. "He is not like his father. She will be the power behind the throne — in fact, she occupies the throne."

16

The prospect of the trip delighted Paré. His curiosity was aroused and his impatience grew at every delay. When everyone and everything was ready, Ruggieri, the Queen's astrologer, decided that the stars were not favorable. When they were favorable, something else went wrong. Finally, on March 25, 1564, the lengthy line of coaches and wagons started on its way. First came a body of halberdiers on foot, then the royal family's carriages, surrounded by steel-clad knights on horseback. Then came more carriages carrying the chaplains, the courtiers, the physicians, surgeons, and apothecaries. Trailing behind, there were many wagons holding pieces of furniture, kitchen utensils, and tableware, as well as the servants.

Snow, rain, sleet, and floods slowed the pace, which was never very fast. With summer came dust, flies,

and mosquitoes to harass them. Sometimes a carriage broke down, a wagon overturned, or a horse ran away. There were a few fractures, injuries, and illnesses, but on the whole the surgeons had little to

do. Paré and his colleagues rode in two comfortable carriages, accompanied by a wagon with their supplies and their surgical instruments.

Before the cortege arrived at a city, they stopped to make preparations. While the Queen left her carriage for a litter decorated with tapestries, the King donned a richly embroidered outfit of silk and velvet and mounted a horse to make an impressive entrance. As they approached, the notables came to meet them with the keys of the city.

That was the moment Paré chose to disappear. Celebrations and festivities annoyed him — he felt they were a waste of time. He preferred visiting the local surgeons in quest of unusual cases and new treatments. He was generally disappointed. The local surgeons' methods were obsolete and their minds far from receptive to new ideas. Some listened politely, but Paré knew he was preaching in the desert. Others refused to hear of anything that was not in the ancients' books and practically threw him out.

At Bar-le-Duc he found the same indifference and the same hostility. He was on his way back to his carriage, discouraged and annoyed, when someone told him of an old barber who was always trying something new. Paré went to see him. Maître Nicolas Picart's shop was like any barber shop, but in a corner was a ladder. At first Paré paid no attention to it. After discussing bone injuries, Picart pointed to the ladder: "Ever use one of these in dislocations of the shoulder?"

Paré felt that here was something new at last. He approached the ladder, and instinctively let his arm hang across a rung.

Picart laughed: "You guessed it. The patient's armpit rests on a rung. He holds a stick in his hand and I pull on it with increasing strength, and the head of the humerus snaps back into the socket."

"Clever," said Paré. "I'll try it. It is better than putting your foot in the armpit and pulling on the arm while the patient is on the floor. Thank you, Maître Picart; today I learned something new."

From Bar-le-Duc the train of carriages turned southward, in the hope of getting to a warmer climate before winter. When they reached Lyons they found the whole region a prey to an epidemic of plague. Physicians and surgeons did not spare their energies, and Paré was not the last to join in the fight. He spent nights and days ministering to the stricken. Careful of his own health, he rubbed his skin with aromatic plants and avoided baths because, he believed, they opened the pores and weakened the body. He was bled regularly and discarded woolens and furred garments for satin and taffeta. These measures all proved worthless: he contracted the disease. But thanks to his robust constitution, he recovered.

In August the cortege left Lyons, reduced to half of what it was at the start. In November they reached Montpellier, the seat of a famous faculty of medicine. Paré, well now and full of renewed energy, continued his inquiries. He felt that a surgeon's education was not complete without a knowledge of the composition of the remedies, and he never failed to call on apothecaries. While in Montpellier, he went to see Maître de Farges, apothecary to the University. He examined the ointments, sniffed the elixirs, tasted the potions. Farges was preparing theriac.

"You are lucky to be able to make your own theriac," said Paré. "I had some once but have never been able to obtain more. I am helpless in treating animal bites. Nothing like theriac for those."

"I agree," said Farges. "So, I decided to make my own when I could not get any more from Venice. You certainly know that all theriac used to come from Venice. They made it once a year and it was the occasion of a ritual celebration, a part of their public life. They used seventy different ingredients in their formula. I have simplified it. Plenty of opiates, naturally, and the main component is the venom of vipers. Come with me: I'll show you my vipers."

Paré went to the back room with him. In glass jars, several snakes were coiled peacefully. "I milk the venom," continued Farges. "It is contained in their mouths near the fangs. You must be careful to catch them on each side of the head."

"Let me try," said Paré, and disregarding Farges's advice, he lifted the lid and plunged his hand into the jar. A viper hissed and lunged at his hand. Paré pulled back, but not fast enough: the fangs penetrated his finger. He sucked the puncture and left at once for his quarters. He ordered a fire in his fireplace in spite of the balmy weather and stayed indoors for fear that, if he got cold, the poison would spread through his body. He ate plenty of meat and drank wine without water. To fight the effect of the venom in the wound itself, he asked Maître de Farges to prepare a lotion made of several herbs boiled in vinegar and urine to bathe his finger. The treatment succeeded.

In the spring the Court left Montpellier for Bayonne, near the Atlantic coast, then went on to Biarritz, in the Basque country. There, Paré saw a whale. He was fascinated by the size of this "monster fish" and was proud to obtain a vertebra, which he took home with him and exhibited in his shop.

After two years Paré was home again, but not for

long. He was called back to Fontainebleau a week after his return. King Charles, tired and feverish, had been bled by a local surgeon. As soon as the lancet had pierced the skin, he had felt a violent shock through his whole arm and now he was in pain and unable to use his arm.

"Why did I let someone else treat me?" moaned the royal patient. "Fetch Maître Paré at once."

For three months Paré applied salves and poultices to the crippled arm. He did not want to blame his colleague, but at the bottom of his heart, he called him stupid and clumsy for having hit a nerve during the procedure.

After such an experience, Charles refused to let his surgeon go. Calls came from many parts of the kingdom but Paré was not permitted to leave. However, when repeated pleas came from the Marquise d'Auret, Charles relented and allowed Paré to go to Mons in the province of Hainaut to attend her husband.

Paré found the patient in bed, a bed which obviously had not been changed for many days. His face was sallow, his eyes sunk in their sockets, his speech barely audible. The surgeon in attendance told Ambroise that a cannon ball had hit the Marquis's leg seven months earlier and that, in spite of unguents and salves, it showed no sign of healing.

Paré approached the bed smiling. His pleasant expression contrasted with the sad faces around him.

"Monsieur le Marquis, the King has sent me. I'll

put all the science that God gave me at your service."

The patient barely reacted. He was in such pain that he had even lost the will to live.

Paré examined the thigh. It was swollen, and from several open sores, streams of pus escaped. He took a silver probe and inserted it in each opening. In one, he hit loose pieces of bone. Another led to a deep and long cavity which extended from the groin to the middle of the thigh. To add to his misery, the Marquis had a large sore on his back.

When the examination was ended, Paré said in a jovial tone, "Monsieur le Marquis, you'll get well, and rapidly." And he left the room. His attitude surprised the surgeons. They watched him as he walked in the garden. He walked slowly, his head bent, his hands joined as if in prayer. In fact, he was praying to be given the right inspiration so that the patient would get well.

An hour later he was back and met with his colleagues. He stroked his beard, squinted slightly, and said, "The Marquis's leg is corrupted by the pus that has collected in the muscles and under the skin. It emits miasmas which go to his heart and his brain and cause fever. The ulcer on his back comes from his seven months in bed. May I ask you when his bed was last changed?"

"Two months ago. We did not dare to move him."

"To obtain a cure one must touch more than a bed."

The remark surprised the surgeons. They laughed.

"At last," said Paré, "you have dropped your gloomy expressions. Remember, never show your concern and your worries. An optimistic attitude is a good remedy. Keep on smiling when we go to see our patient."

"What would you advise, Maître Paré?"

Paré answered curtly, "Why didn't you enlarge those openings to drain that mud from the depths? That's what I'm going to do. Then the leg must be kept warm to avoid gangrene. We'll surround it with warm stones and wrap it up in many layers of linen cloth. For the bedsore I'll give you an ointment to apply, and we'll have him rest on a hollow cushion to relieve the pressure on his back. After I have opened all these cavities we'll put the Marquis in a clean bed and give him plenty to eat—meats, eggs, and don't forget, wine without water to make him strong."

The result was almost miraculous. The patient spent a restful night and his condition improved rapidly. Two months later he was walking. As Paré left, with a goodly sum of money and a big diamond on his finger, a gift from the Marquise, the patient expressed his gratitude and admiration. Paré shook his head: "I don't deserve such praise, Monsieur le Marquis. I treated you, God healed you."

17

It was the end of a warm summer afternoon — August 22, 1572. Maître Paré, arrayed in velvet and satin, a stiff lace ruff around his neck, was riding home from the Louvre where he had attended the festivities celebrating the marriage of Henri de Bourbon, King of Navarre, and Marguerite, Charles IX's sister.

He looked at the limp foliage, at the brown grass. "What a day," he reflected, wiping his face. "I'll always remember the summer of 1572 as the hottest and driest I ever lived through." He patted the mare's neck: "We'll be home soon."

At his door, he dismounted swiftly. Even at sixty-two he had not lost the agility of his younger years, but his age showed in his heavier figure and his receding gray hair. He handed the bridle to his stable-boy and entered.

Jehanne greeted him. She threw her arms around him. "At last," she said. "Tell me all about the wedding."

He returned her kiss and laughed: "Let me come in and sit down first."

She clapped her hands to call a servant. "Bring a jug of cool wine for the master," she ordered, and then she began asking him about the dresses, the jewels, the comportment of the royal bride.

"She did not seem happy. At Notre-Dame, when she was asked the ritual question, she did not answer. King Charles was back of her. He quickly put his hand on her neck to make her nod the yes she would not say. As for the dresses and jewels, I did not notice them."

Jehanne insisted, and he suddenly became serious. The furrow between his brows grew deeper, and his brown eyes darkened. "Do you understand what this union means, a marriage between a Protestant king and a Catholic princess? It means the end of the deadly religious feud that has racked the kingdom."

She too became serious: "It means much."

Before he could continue, the clatter of galloping hoofs was heard outside. They both looked out the window. A horse had stopped at their door and a man entered. "Orders from the King. Maître Paré, His Majesty requests your presence at Admiral Coligny's home. The Admiral has been felled by a pistol shot fired from a window as he left the palace."

Paré started. Admiral Coligny, the chief of the

Huguenots, respected by friends and foes, honored with the King's friendship — shot in ambush. The feud was not over. While waiting for his horse to be saddled again, he questioned the emissary: "Do you know who shot him?"

"Yes. Maurevel."

Paré repeated, "Maurevel?" He understood, but preferred to keep his opinion to himself. Maurevel's hand had been armed by Queen Catherine. He was her close companion, and her hatred for the Admiral was well known.

They both sprang into their saddles and pushed their horses on in spite of the stifling heat. The sky was dark. Silent lightning flashed in the distance. The air was heavy with the menace of a storm.

At the Admiral's house in the Rue de l'Arbre Sec, near the Louvre, the King's envoy left. Paré dismounted while the young stableboy, tears trickling down his face, took hold of the reins. "Oh, Maître Paré," he said, "please save my master."

Paré, touched by the boy's sorrow, put his hand on his head. "Have faith and pray," he said, and went up the stone stairs. Before he could lift the brass knocker Nicolas Muss, Coligny's old servant, had opened the door. "My master is saved now that you are here," he said, his voice trembling with repressed sobs. Tense with anger and grief, Paré followed him.

The Admiral was resting in an armchair. He had refused to lie down. Near him stood Pastor Merlin, his spiritual advisor. Paré bowed to the pastor and had a few cheerful words for the patient before examining his injuries. They were serious, but not dangerous. The right hand had been shattered by the bullet and the left humerus was broken. He probed both wounds, removed the splinters skillfully, and then stood silent for a moment, stroking his beard.

The Admiral tried to read his thoughts, but Paré's eyes were closed. "What do you think, Maître Paré?"

"I'll have to amputate your forefinger at the joint. As to your arm, I'll set it in a sling."

Barely was the operation finished when the King arrived, anxious to see his injured friend and tell him of his indignation over the cowardly attack. He came in on tiptoe, fearing the worst. The flickering candles cast an eerie light on the Admiral's pallid face. His shallow breathing was the only sign of life in his motionless body.

"Will he recover?" the King asked.

"He will," Paré replied.

"I'll punish the man who dared to attack you," the King said to the Admiral, who had opened his eyes. "And I'll pray for your recovery, of which I have no doubt since Maître Paré is attending you. You will heal."

"With God's help," answered Paré.

The following day he went to the Louvre to report to the King. Courtiers were waiting in the halls and assailed him with questions. All seemed interested in the Admiral's condition, but whether they were pleased or not at hearing he was not in danger remained carefully hidden. Charles voiced satisfaction when told the Admiral had spent a restful night. In an optimistic mood, Paré left the royal chamber.

A page was waiting for him at the door: "My master, the King of Navarre, wants to see you."

Paré was not surprised that Henri de Bourbon, a Huguenot, should be concerned about Coligny, and he went with the page.

Henri had inherited the vivid and exuberant personality of his father Antoine, but today he was in a somber mood. His sparkling eyes had assumed a grave expression. "Be careful, Maître Paré," he said, "this attack is only a beginning. Coligny's enemies won't relent. His doom is written and most probably mine is also."

"But, Your Majesty, you have married the King's sister. Your marriage is the symbol and the assurance of the union between the two religions."

"Don't let my marriage deceive you. Like everybody else, if you were at Notre-Dame, you must have seen that I was not agreeable to the bride. My marriage does not herald an understanding between the two religions. It is a political move on my royal brother-in-law's part to appease both parties. It does not mean peace. You are a man of science; you are not used to palace intrigues. That is the reason I wanted to warn you. The Admiral is not safe yet and those who have befriended him are in danger also."

"The King visited him last evening and was pleased at my report this morning."

"The King could be easily swayed. He'll do as his mother says. Be careful."

Paré was alarmed. Henri's words had convinced him of the impending danger. He walked through the great halls of the Louvre, wondering about the future. From afar he saw a heavily draped figure coming toward him: the Queen Mother. He stopped, but she did not as was her custom when she saw her son's surgeon. Instead, she replied to his respectful bow with a quick nod and walked on.

Paré smiled bitterly as the swish of her dress died in the distance: "She alone did not inquire about the Admiral. I'd have thought her to be shrewder. She must be sure of herself not to have tried to disguise her feelings. The King of Navarre is right — the Admiral is in danger. I'll go and stay with him tonight."

He left his shop early, but chose to walk instead of ride. The streets were deserted — it was Saturday night. The Parisians did not observe the old custom of *la veillée* as did the people in the provinces, but they closed their shops early.

Paré crossed the courtyard, climbed the stone stairs and pounded the knocker several times before getting an answer. Finally the door opened slowly. Pastor Merlin was before him.

"How is the Admiral?"

"Resting comfortably," said the Pastor. "I'm alone with him."

"The servants?"

"They will be back soon. Nicolas is with his master. As for the menial who takes care of the stable, he is a papist and his name is Bartholomew."

Seeing the question in Maître Paré's eyes, Merlin continued: "You may not know, but tomorrow the Catholics celebrate the feast of Saint Bartholomew, the Apostle. So our Bartholomew has been permitted to go to his family for the day."

"I intend to stay with the Admiral tonight," said Paré.

"So do I," answered Merlin.

The patient greeted his surgeon with a warm smile. Merlin stayed in the entrance hall and Paré propped himself in an armchair. But he could not sleep. It was not the thought of possible danger that kept him awake, but the realization of the futility of his beloved profession before man's intent to kill. "We try to heal and preserve God's gift of life — the greatest of them all — but a criminal hand annihilates it. Why? We are taught to love one another and all I have seen since my youth is hatred. It leads to war, where innocents are pitched against each other, and personal revenges. What for?"

Long before dawn his restless sleep was broken by the pealing of bells.

"The tocsin! A fire? Where?"

The Admiral had risen from his bed: "Those are the bells of Saint-Germain-l'Auxerrois, the palace's parish. Why so early?"

Cries of "Kill! Kill!" and the trampling of feet answered the bells. Gunfire broke out and screams filled the air. To thwart a possible attack, the servants piled furniture at the front entrance. Merlin and Nicolas rushed to the Admiral's room. Through the windows they saw hordes carrying pistols and torches, bent on a frenzy of killing. Houses were set on fire; bodies were hurled into the gutter — men, women, children. Death was everywhere.

Soon heavy banging on the front door made them realize the situation.

"Flee," said Coligny, "flee, the three of you. Flee by the roof while it is still possible. You can't save my life. I will meet my murderers standing."

Nicolas had fallen on his knees: "God have mercy on us. I'll stay with you."

Paré and Merlin ran up the stairs. They had not reached the garret when a noise made them stop. A window had been shattered at the rear of the house. Merlin rushed to the garret and disappeared onto the roof. Paré bent over the banister. Two men were coming up. He recognized one of them as the King's envoy who had taken him to the Admiral's house the day before. With him was a guard from the Louvre. The envoy looked up. He called: "Maître Paré, I have an order from the King to bring you to his apartments. We went to your home. Your wife said you were here. No time to lose. Follow us."

Paré and his two companions climbed onto the roof. They looked down. In the courtyard lay the

body of Nicolas in a pool of blood. Below them the Admiral, pierced by many swords, was dangling from the window sill. One of the assassins pushed him over and he fell on the cobblestones with a heavy thud.

Paré repressed a sob: "They murdered him!"

"No time for pity. The King wants you."

The two men, their swords drawn in case of attack, dragged Paré, bewildered, toward the palace. They entered through a side door and ushered him to the King's bedchamber. Paré caught a glimpse of Queen Catherine watching from a window the work of destruction wrought by her order.

King Charles was sitting on his bed, disheveled and haggard. He jumped to his feet when Paré en-

tered, as if ready to defend himself against an attack.
The room was dark. The curtains were drawn over
the windows. Paré parted them: "Your Majesty, one
word from you and this carnage will stop."

"Close them!" cried Charles. "I don't want to see.
I don't want to hear." He flung himself on the bed
and buried his head in the pillows.

Paré walked to the bed. He stood there, his face
flushed with anger. "Why?"

Charles raised his head and seized Paré's wrist: "I
had to. My crown was at stake. She wrenched this
order from me."

She: the shrewd Queen, in whose expert hands
her twenty-two-year-old son was but a toy.

Paré said in a low tone, "Admiral Coligny is dead."

The King gave a long sigh: "He was my friend and I killed him." Suddenly his eyes took on a savage glare. He ran to the window, tore the curtains away, and pounded on the glass: "Kill them!" he screamed. "All of them, so that not one is left to reproach me for the death of his brother."

By the end of that day — August 24, 1572 — the Saint Bartholomew massacre had claimed more than two thousand victims and had left spiritual wounds that could not be healed.

18

His eyes still filled with the horrors he had witnessed, his heart heavy with grief, Paré tried to forget in a renewal of activities. He read, he wrote, he studied, and little by little, the warm atmosphere of his home quieted the bitterness that had invaded his soul. He enjoyed the company of his wife, although he rarely found her receptive to his ideas or interested in his search for progress. Catherine, the only survivor of his three children, was growing and promised to be a pretty but headstrong girl. Another Jehanne, the daughter of his late brother the coffer maker, completed his family.

It was at that time that his *Books of Surgery* were published, with a revised chapter on the wounds by arquebuses. His search for further knowledge went on persistently. He often repeated that one life is not long enough to gather all we need to know. "We should not waste any of the precious hours the Lord has granted us."

His quest for knowledge led him to try a cold cautery which a philosopher had given him without revealing its nature. It was the size of a pea and looked like a block of salt. Paré looked at it, rolled it in his fingers: "A cold cautery indeed! I must try it."

One of his servants volunteered when assured that it would be painless. Paré applied the tiny stone to his arm, covered it with velvet and left it in place for a half-hour. There was no pain, but when the dressing was removed the skin was found to be ulcerated. A deep hole had formed under the mysterious action of the stone.

This worried Paré. "I must know the nature of this caustic and the time it should be left on the skin." He asked the philosopher, who refused to give any information: "This is my secret. My formula is not for publication. You believe in telling everything. I don't."

"If Galen, Vigo, and all those who lived in the past had refused to reveal the sum of their experience, the results of their observations, we would be as ignorant as our forefathers one thousand years ago."

This wise remark did not shake the obstinacy of the philosopher. Paré was vexed. "Here is a valuable discovery," he thought, "and because its inventor is a stubborn old mule the world is to be deprived of a precious remedy. How can I make him open his mouth?" He wondered: "A gift of money? That worked in Italy when I wanted to obtain the formula for a balm, but this man is a philosopher. He might be offended." Paré stroked his beard several times. This familiar gesture seemed to inspire him: "The philosopher's clothing is shabby, his shoes worn out."

A few days later he called on the philosopher with several yards of velvet under his arm. "I thought you might be able to use this," he said casually, "and if I knew the size of your shoes . . ."

The philosopher's eyes sparkled. Paré had hit upon the right idea.

"Since your last visit, Maître Paré, I have thought about your request. It is most reasonable, and I have come to the conclusion that you could make good use of my invention. But first, you must swear not to reveal its formula."

Maître Paré swore and the philosopher began dictating: "Reduce to ashes, pods of the horse bean to the extent of three pounds. Mix with three pounds of oak-bark ashes. Add six quarts of river water and one pound of scum from wine kegs. Add four ounces of alum. Put this mixture into a cauldron and boil it. Skim it and boil the residue again until it is reduced to a small lump of hard stone."

Paré wrote feverishly. He could not have known that the innocent-looking stone was nothing else but a lump of potassium hydroxide, a powerful caustic. He was happy. The yards of velvet had not been bought in vain and the coveted recipe was even worth a pair of shoes. Now that he had the formula, he could experiment.

To keep abreast of new discoveries, Paré read everything of interest. One day, as he was browsing in a bookshop, a treatise attracted his attention: *The Nature and Cure of Wounds by Pistols, Arquebuses, and Other Firing Rods.* The author was not a surgeon but a physician, Julien Le Paumier, Regent at the Faculty of Paris.

Paré was surprised and indignant: "A physician who has never come in contact with the wounded and would not even touch a dressing. How dare he write on a subject of which he knows nothing?"

Paré thumbed through the book, angry at its author and annoyed at his inability to read it. It was in Latin. The title he understood, but the rest was too much for him. He bought the book, had it translated, and began to read the manuscript with eagerness.

His anger increased tenfold when he saw what Le Paumier had to say. This physician had the impudence to attack him, Ambroise Paré, whose surgical competence and skill were well known and widely appreciated. Of course, Le Paumier was wise enough not to mention any name, but the object of his attacks was obvious: "A certain person dared to condemn the cauterization of bleeding vessels after an amputation, a procedure recommended by the ancients and approved by all surgeons."

Paré felt like tearing the book apart. "The audacity of the man!" he said aloud, pounding the manuscript. He got up and went to the window, opened it, and breathed deeply. "This should cool off the vapors of anger that might make me do a foolish thing like destroying these pages. I must finish reading them, no matter how much it infuriates me."

He went back to the manuscript: "Sewing up the vessels has been boldly tried in spite of wiser and well-established opinions. There is more danger in ligating the vessels than in cauterizing them. It is done with a needle. A needle is sharp and could touch a nerve. This would cause intractable pain. Furthermore, the damming of blood would cause inflammation, which in turn would precipitate convulsions, and convulsions mean death.

"This person affirms that pinching the vessels, pulling them from the depth where they have retracted, and inserting a needle into healthy flesh causes less pain than the application of a red-hot iron. This is a grave error. If anyone has survived this cruel procedure he can thank God for having been cured by a miracle. Ligation of the vessels should be left to the hands of the executioner in a torture chamber. It does not belong to the hands of a surgeon worthy of the name."

Paré stopped reading. His face was grim, his fists clenched: "Torture chamber. I wish this physician could hear the thanks of the wounded I have treated and see the results."

He went on, attracted in spite of himself. In the last chapter Le Paumier advocated a new treatment

— his own invention, he said — to cure swelling around the eyes: "Shave the head and make a transverse incision from the left temple to the right and be careful to spare the fibers of the temporal muscles."

It sounded familiar. Paré searched through his books and found the description of the "new" treatment, almost word for word, in a treatise by Paul of Aegina and Abulcasis. "A plagiarist, Le Paumier. You are nothing but a shameless plagiarist."

He grabbed a quill, sharpened it, and wrote thirty pages without replacing it, in spite of its scratchiness. He took the pages to a publisher, who printed them, and a copy of the pamphlet was sent to Le Paumier.

Le Paumier shrugged his shoulders: "A member of the College of Surgeons writing in French. Should I lower myself and answer his demented criticism?" He thought it over, then decided it warranted a rebuke and charged another barber to pen the reply. Maître Paré was attacked for daring to express such ideas and in French. "This person thinks he is the first surgeon in the world, and in fact he knows nothing. I have in my bag an ounce of an antidote against those swollen with pride and conceit who forget their duty and the respect they owe to their superiors."

By the time Paré read these lines he had acquired a certain philosophy and chose to ignore the attack. Reward came later when his *Books of Surgery* met with wide approval and had to be reprinted several times. Le Paumier's treatise sold poorly and most of the copies lay forgotten in bookshops.

19

Maître Paré pushed open the door of his shop with a weary hand. It was early morning. He had spent a sleepless night at the Louvre, watching over the almost demented Charles IX, who was obsessed with memories of the Saint Bartholomew massacre. A lone apprentice was sweeping the floor and preparing razors and curling irons for the day's work. He stopped at the sight of his master: "How he has changed in a few days!" Paré's shoulders stooped, his step was heavy, his face drawn. He answered the apprentice's *"bonjour"* distractedly, threw his bag on a table, and walked listlessly to the back room. He stopped for a moment before closing the door behind him. The house was silent. The familiar greeting he almost expected would never be heard again. Jehanne was dead. He went to his desk and sat down. With an impatient gesture he pushed away the papers and books before him. He rested his elbows on the table and buried his face in his hands.

One by one the events of the last days which had changed his life filed before him. They brought tears to his eyes: "I was powerless. I did not know what to do. After saving so many lives I could not save hers." He raised his head. The sun played on a jar where leeches clung to the glass walls. "Poor Jehanne. She could not bear looking at them, and how I used to tease her." A sad smile lifted the corner of his mouth for an instant at the thought of her often-expressed repulsion. "Jehanne . . . What a good mother she was, quiet in happiness and in sorrow." He remembered her submission to God's will when one after the other their little sons were carried to their graves. "I also accepted my Lord's decision, but it was hard. All I have left is a daughter. Who will continue my work?"

The wan face of the dying Jehanne flashed before him: "Ambroise, who will take care of you after I'm gone? You should not stay alone. Catherine needs a mother. At fourteen, one does. Our little niece needs a mother also." And for the first time, the thought of a second marriage came to Paré. He repressed it as almost sacrilegious, but it imposed itself again and again. "A son, perhaps a little son, God willing."

On January 18, 1574, less than two months after Jehanne's death, Paré married Jacqueline Rousselet, the daughter of a rich bourgeois attached to the royal stables.

Eighteen months later a daughter was born — Anne. Jacqueline was to be the mother of six children in nine years, four girls and two boys. The boys and two of the girls died in infancy. Paré's dream of a son was never to be fulfilled.

Still, neither grief nor happiness deterred him from his devotion to the art of surgery. No patient was too poor or too far away to be attended, and besides his interest in the patient's welfare, Paré felt that each case was one more opportunity to try to understand the human body.

Besides the increasing demands of his clientele, his duties as First Royal Surgeon were becoming more absorbing. The King's health was failing rapidly. In strenuous hunts and other violent exercise, Charles was trying to escape from the visions of maimed faces that haunted him. In a last effort to evade the tragic memories associated with the Louvre, he left it for the Château of Vincennes, far from the center of Paris. Tortured by guilt, his strength ebbing, he demanded Paré's continual presence at his side. And on May 30, 1574, Charles IX died, a victim of remorse and tuberculosis.

The next day found Maître Paré and the other surgeons of the royal household in the basement of the Louvre, where the King's body had been transferred. They had finished embalming the cadaver, and as it was taken away to lie in state they discussed their findings. "The cavities we saw in the left lung," said Paré, "were certainly due to the

King's excessive use of the hunting horn at a time when he was coughing and complaining of pains in his chest. I repeatedly advised him to discontinue such practice, but His Majesty refused to listen."

They all agreed. Paré counted on his fingers: "François, first of the name; Henri the Second; François the Second; and now Charles the Ninth. Four kings I have served, four kings I have buried."

"Who will be our next king?" said one. "I don't think Queen Catherine's third son will want to leave the throne of Poland."

"Then her youngest son will inherit the crown, if he can be persuaded to abandon his courtship of Queen Elizabeth of England."

"With no other male heir," said Paré, "our next king will be Henri de Navarre."

"A Protestant? Impossible."

"He abjured."

Laughter greeted these words. Everyone knew that Henri de Bourbon, King of Navarre, had renounced his faith on the night of the Saint Bartholomew massacre, but no one had taken him seriously, Henri less than anyone. Back in his tiny kingdom at the foot of the Pyrenees, he held that he had abjured to save his life and that a promise made under duress was not binding.

The discussion between those who approved of Henri and those who did not threatened to become bitter. "A picture in small of what will happen in the kingdom," thought Paré, and he changed the subject: "I hope a younger man is called in to take over my charge. I'm well past sixty and I want to spend my last years revising my notes and publishing my experiments. Goodbye, Messieurs." He took his instruments and left.

20

Relieved of his duties in the absence of a king, Paré thought he would be able to work in peace, but now he had to face the open hostility of the Faculty of Medicine. When the first edition of his *Complete Works* was published in April 1575, Gourmelen, Dean of the Faculty, whose own writings had failed, looked for a way to discredit "that barber." He found an old document dated May 3, 1535, that forbade the printing of any medical treatise unless it had been approved by the University. Gourmelen was elated. Paré had neglected this formality, perhaps through ignorance, perhaps for good reason. Here was a first line of attack — the rest would be easy. Gourmelen began campaigning. He met with members of the University; he went to the College of Surgeons; he even appealed to the Parliament to ban Paré's book: "It has never been sanctioned — a grave omission and a breach of ethics — and it never will be. Its descriptions of the human body are immodest, the chapters on treatments and remedies are the work of a plagiarist, the results of what the author calls innovations are deliberate lies. Furthermore this treatise is written in French, which means that anybody could read it, and we all know how quickly errors can spread. I demand that it be burned."

Jealous colleagues jumped at the opportunity and banded with the alderman and the Provost of the Merchant Guilds. Maître Paré was declared *"impudentissimus, imperitissimus et maximus temerarius"* — very impudent, very arrogant, and most foolhardy — and was summoned before the Parliament.

Immediately he hired a lawyer, Jean Bautru, who asked that the hearing be postponed to give them time to map out their defense. Soon a pamphlet appeared: "In answer to the calumnies against my work by physicians and surgeons." One by one, the accusations were disproved.

"Your main objection is that I write in French and in terms that are easy for anyone to understand. Hence the physicians are afraid of two things: that they will not be consulted as often and also that the barbers, more learned in their art through my teachings, will encroach on their field. May I add that Hippocrates wrote in his native tongue?

"What I say about the monsters and deformities is in effect taken from the ancients. Quoting is not plagiarism.

"Why are my descriptions of the human body declared immodest in 1575 when they were printed in my previous book in 1573 and the Faculty did not raise any objection at that time?

"I still insist that sulfur cures intestinal worms and that antimony has brought good results in the treatment of the plague. It is a drastic treatment, I concede it, but Hippocrates wrote that for a strong malady you should use a strong remedy.

"I still insist that, after many trials, I found the horn of the unicorn useless in the treatment of poisoning.

"As to the balm called Aegyptiac, how could it be accused of being a dangerous remedy when it is made of alum, salt, honey, and vinegar, all substances which never harmed anybody when taken individually?

"Now a word about Egyptian mummy powder. I have been asked many times why I don't prescribe it. Not long ago a patient expressed surprise at being cured without having been given the powder. The so-called Egyptian mummy powder does not come from Egypt. It is made right here. Some unscrupulous persons, because of the wide demand for it, make a practice of bribing the executioner to obtain the bones of dead criminals. They crush them, mix them with shoemaker's wax, and sell this product as true Egyptian mummy powder. This revelation should make anyone think before prescribing such a foul concoction.

"I have discarded long-accepted remedies because

they have no value. Such is the common belief that spitting into the mouth of a frog will cure a cough, and also that wrapping one's forehead with a hangman's rope will relieve a headache.

"It is time for someone to speak up and condemn such practices. It is time for someone to write of these fallacies in French so that their real value is known."

The trial took place on July 14, 1575. The session was stormy. After hearing both parties the Parliament upheld the decree of May 1535, condemned Paré to pay the expenses, and postponed the announcement of a verdict to a later meeting. This meeting never took place. Events of importance overshadowed the trial.

Henri de Valois, King of Poland, had left his capital and arrived in Paris to take the throne of France. One of his first moves was to summon Maître Paré.

Paré was received privately by Queen Catherine. He felt an aura of happiness as soon as he was admitted to her presence. The furrows of grief that had altered her face had disappeared. Her bulging eyes seemed more lively. There was a hint of color in her waxen skin. Paré looked at her hands as he bowed — they were still beautiful.

"Maître Paré, it is the King's desire and mine also that you should continue to occupy the charge of First Surgeon. That is all I want to say. Go and see my son. He will tell you more."

"I should be flattered and happy," thought Paré
as he left for the King's apartments, "but I'm not. I
had hoped to be free from this forever."

A strong smell of perfume almost overcame him
at the door of the King's chamber. Henri III, reclin-
ing on his bed, was sampling different odors on lace
handkerchiefs. Several small dogs were romping on
the satin coverlet. Near the window, a cage held some
brightly colored birds.

Henri stopped when he saw Ambroise Paré. He carefully replaced the vials on a table and his face contracted in a nervous smile. He gestured with his heavily jeweled hands and spoke in an affected, high-pitched voice: "I know my mother has already told you that you are to continue your post as First Surgeon. She wanted to do it herself to show the deep esteem and, I dare say, the affection she has for you. To me falls the pleasant task of telling you that I have named you a member of my Council in recognition of your devotion to my father and my two brothers."

Squinting slightly, Paré looked at him: "So, this is the Queen's favorite son. At last he occupies the throne and she is happy. But what a puppet he is! His pointed beard hides a weak chin, like his brothers'. He is as full of mannerisms as when he was a boy, even more so." The contrast with the plain-looking, energetic, outspoken Henri de Navarre suggested itself — too bad he had not ascended the throne.

The opportune arrival of Henri de Valois, now Henri III, and the news of Maître Paré's elevation to the Council silenced the Parliament and the forthcoming verdict was never delivered.

The open controversy, as well as the importance and novelty of its contents, contributed to the success of the *Five Books of Surgery*. They sold well, and so did Maître Paré's other writings. This encouraged him. He read more, he wrote more. Births and deaths at home incited him to take refuge in his work. Three babies in three years, Anne, Ambroise, and Marie, and two deaths, Ambroise and Marie. No son to continue after him.

In 1578, the last edition of the *Five Books of Surgery* was exhausted, but not the demand for it. Paré conferred with the editor, revised his text, and a new printing was prepared. This time, wiser from experience, he submitted the manuscript to the Faculty. A committee of ten physicians was named and the treatise was accepted with few modifications. The chapter treating of fevers was omitted. It was agreed that the subject belonged to the physicians and not to the surgeons, but Paré managed to diffuse most of its substance through the rest of the pages. Two new chapters were added, one on "Animals and the Supremacy of Man," the other on "Wounds by Various Firearms," which was a development of his first book on the same subject.

In 1582 followed the "Discourse on the Mummy, the Venoms, the Unicorn, and the Plague." This aroused more controversy and much criticism because it questioned the existence of the unicorn. There was an exchange of pamphlets between Paré and the members of the Faculty.

In 1585 came the fourth edition of Maître Ambroise Paré's *Complete Works,* to which was added the "Apology" in defense of the ligation of blood vessels. His conclusion was impressive in its dignity: "I publish this Apology so that everyone will know the path I have followed all my life. I do not think that any man, no matter how captious, will criticize me, for I speak the truth. Results prove the legitimacy of a cause, and my sincerity is my arm against calumny."

This was the year after he had buried his third son. Anne and little Catherine survived and also the first Catherine, the headstrong daughter of his first wife, who had broken all contact with her father after her marriage.

Paré, though advanced in years, continued to attend his practice, answer attacks, and go to the Louvre whenever his duty to the King or to his Council called for his presence.

In 1589 Henri III fell under the knife of a murderer while residing at Saint-Cloud, near Paris. Paré did not attend the King in his last moments and he was not summoned to embalm the body. He had not followed the Court; his age prevented him from traveling even a short distance.

It was a warm October afternoon. Alone in his room, Ambroise Paré thought of the past; he reviewed his well-used life. He had no bitternesss against those who had fought his ideas and criticized his discoveries. "Their attacks made me work harder and study more. Everything happens for the best. The Lord has his plan when he sends us sorrows and joys." He looked around him. The leeches were still clinging to the walls of their jar. On one shelf there was a flying fish, a stuffed bird of paradise, the beak of a toucan; in a corner, the skeleton of an ostrich. The house was silent except for the twittering of sparrows outside. Paré opened the window and put a few crumbs on the balcony. "I should not do this," he said. "People are hungry — but you are God's creatures also and you should live."

People were hungry. Since August, the 200,000 inhabitants of Paris had been besieged by the forces of Henri de Navarre. Lawful heir to the childless Valois, designated as his successor by the dying Henri III, he was not accepted by the French, and at the head of an army, he was trying to conquer his kingdom. Later, when he realized that his religion was the only obstacle between himself and the crown, he would repudiate his return to Protestantism after his hasty conversion during the night of the Saint Bartholomew massacre. He would solemnly embrace the Catholic faith on July 25, 1593, in the cathedral of Saint-Denis, near Paris, to become Henri IV.

For a while, Paré watched the sparrows fighting for the bread crumbs. Then he felt that a walk would be pleasant on such a clear day. He took his cane and went toward the Seine. His eighty years weighed heavily on him. His beard was white, his step unsteady, his shoulders slouching, but his eyes still burned with love for his fellow men and interest in their welfare. "How many will appreciate this beautiful day?" he mused as he headed for the Pont Saint-Michel. "Parisians are dying by the hundreds. Is a kingdom worth the life of one man?"

At the other end of the bridge a crowd had gathered. He approached. Men and women surrounded a priest, His Eminence the Archbishop of Paris. Their haggard faces, their anguished eyes showed their misery. Human suffering had always aroused Paré's compassion. He straightened his shoulders, held his head high, and addressed the prelate in a strong voice: "Your Eminence, don't you see they are starving? Help them if you want our Lord to help you. God's order is peace, not war. Use your power to give us peace. The people of Paris, all the people of France, want peace."

The Archbishop listened. He lifted his hand in a blessing and departed, his shoulders humped, his eyes veiled with tears, while Maître Ambroise Paré, erect, his face reflecting pity, was acclaimed by those who had recognized him.

The blockade was lifted the following month, but Ambroise Paré, bedridden, was too weak to rejoice.

EPILOGUE

Christmas Eve, 1590. Paris was cloaked in a white mantle. Church bells were pealing merrily. *Noël* again in a liberated city.

A lone man was plowing through the drifts in a deserted street, a lantern in his hand. He raised it before each house, looked up, and kept going. At last he stopped. "Here it is," he said. He pounded the knocker several times. A woman opened the door. "Maître Paré," said the man. "I want Maître Paré to come and see my little daughter. She is very sick."

The woman looked at him with compassion. Her voice trembled as she answered, "Maître Paré died four days ago." And the door closed with a heavy thud.

The man stood still for a moment as if he had not understood. "Maître Paré . . ." He repressed a sob. "My poor little girl . . ." And he retraced his steps in the snow, repeating, "Maître Paré is dead . . . Maître Paré is dead . . ."